SkillBuilder Workbook

Reading • Literature • Vocabulary • Writing

McDougal Littell

BRIDGES TO
LITERATURE

LEVEL 3

D1221936

🦅 McDougal Littell
A DIVISION OF HOUGHTON MIFFLIN COMPANY

ISBN-13: 978-0-618-95353-0   ISBN-10: 0-618-95353-1

Printed in the United States of America.

1 2 3 4 5 6 7 8 9 — MDO — 11 10 09 08 07

Table of Contents

Comprehension, Literary, and Vocabulary SkillBuilders

Table of Contents (continued)

Table of Contents *(continued)*

Writing Prompts and Templates

Table of Contents *(continued)*

To the Teacher

This workbook accompanies the *Bridges to Literature* program and provides additional skills practice in the program's four focus areas: reading comprehension, literature, vocabulary, and writing. The first section is organized by selection, and contains SkillBuilder pages for reading, literature, and vocabulary. These pages are duplicated in the Teacher's Edition for use as copymasters. Also included in the Teacher's Edition are mini-lessons that allow the teacher to provide direct instruction for each skill, as well as answer keys for SkillBuilder pages.

The writing section contains a set of three pages for each unit. The first page contains writing prompts tied to the unit selections. The last of these is a Unit Writing Assignment, which allows students to apply what they have learned from reading several selections. The last two pages of each set provide a writing template to guide students as they prepare the Unit Assignment and a page of revising guidelines and editing tips to help them improve their final draft.

At the end of the workbook look for the Independent Reading List for books students might enjoy reading on their own. To help students select books appropriate for their reading levels, each book is annotated with its DRP score. Encourage students to use the Reading Log to keep a record of their readings and the Personal Word List as a study tool for increasing their vocabularies.

SkillBuilders

THE TELL-TALE HEART *(pages 4–13)*

Visualizing

Visualizing means creating a picture in your mind. Trying to see what the writer describes makes you more aware of the details that are given. Sometimes drawing a sketch of a scene is helpful.

Here are two paragraphs from "The Tell-Tale Heart." One describes what the narrator does. The other describes what the narrator sees. Below are two boxes. Sketch the picture you imagine from each paragraph in each box.

When I had waited a long time, very patiently, without hearing him lie down, I decided to open a little—a very, very little—crack in the lantern. So I opened it—you cannot imagine how carefully—until a single dim ray, like the thread of the spider, shot out from the crack and fell precisely upon the vulture eye.

It was open—wide, wide open—and I grew furious as I gazed upon it. I saw it perfectly clearly—all a dull blue. It had a hideous veil over it that chilled the very center of my bones. But I could see nothing of the old man's face or body, for I had directed the ray as if by instinct, precisely on that eye.

Paragraph 1: What narrator does	Paragraph 2: What narrator sees

Read each detail below. Decide whether the detail was described in **paragraph 1** or **paragraph 2**. Write the number 1 or 2 next to the detail.

_____ one ray of light comes out   _____ the eye is dull blue

_____ the eye is open   _____ a beam of light in the dark

_____ the eye has a film over it   _____ no body is visible, only an eye

_____ the lantern is open a tiny crack   _____ a ray like a spider's thread

THE TELL-TALE HEART *(pages 4–13)*

Plot

The **plot** of a story is the series of events that make up the story. In a horror story, most of the plot builds up to the climax. The events that build up are called the **rising action.** The **climax** is the most exciting part of the story, or the turning point. Often a horror story ends at the climax.

A. Write a number, 1–8, on each line to show the order in which the events happened in the story.

_____ a. The narrator opens the lantern and sees that the old man's eye is open.

_____ b. Police come to the door because neighbors heard the old man's cry.

_____ c. The narrator kills the old man.

_____ d. The noise of the beating heart finally makes the narrator tell the police what he's done.

_____ e. The narrator claims he is not mad and will prove it by telling his story.

_____ f. The narrator becomes frightened by the old man's eye.

_____ g. The narrator welcomes the police officers and invites them to sit and talk.

_____ h. The narrator cuts up the old man's body and hides the parts under the floor.

B. Use the letters a–h from above to complete these questions.

1. Which two events are part of the **introduction?**_____

2. Which event is the **climax**—the most exciting part or the turning point of the story?

_____

3. Which five events are part of the **rising action?** Write the letters in the order that the events

happened. _____

THE TELL-TALE HEART *(pages 4–13)*

Multiple-Meaning Words

Many words have **multiple meanings,** or more than one meaning. You can often choose the correct meaning by noticing how the word is used in the passage, or context.

A. Read each sentence and the definitions for the underlined word. Then write the letter of the correct definition for the sentence.

_____ **1.** It took me an hour to place my whole <u>head</u> within the opening.
　　a. the top part of the body in humans and many animals
　　b. a person who is in charge

_____ **2.** I placed my <u>hand</u> upon the heart.
　　a. a member of a group of workers or a ship's crew
　　b. the part of the human body attached to the end of the arm

_____ **3.** The heart <u>beat</u> on with a muffled sound.
　　a. hit or struck　　　　　　　b. pulsed or throbbed

_____ **4.** A single dim ray <u>shot</u> out from the crack in the lantern.
　　a. wounded with a weapon　　b. projected swiftly

B. Choose the correct meaning for each underlined word in the sentences below.

_____ **1.** Mr. Conklin invited the <u>board</u> to tour the new factory.

_____ **2.** Many of the <u>boards</u> were warped, so we couldn't use them for our bookcase.

　　a. board: a long, flat piece of sawed wood
　　b. board: a group of people who control a business, school, or organization

_____ **3.** If their <u>well</u> goes dry, the villagers will have to walk two miles for water.

_____ **4.** Everyone scored <u>well</u> on the recent quiz.

　　c. well: a hole sunk into the earth to tap underground water
　　d. well: in a good or proper manner

_____ **5.** The visitors <u>beat</u> the home team by only two points.

_____ **6.** Doesn't your heart <u>beat</u> faster when that scary movie music starts?

　　e. beat: to pound or throb in a regular pattern
　　f. beat: to defeat in a game

THE TELL-TALE HEART *(pages 4–13)*

Words to Know

vulture   cautious   mortal   precisely

A. Fill in each blank with the correct word from the list above.

1. A very careful person is _____ and tries to avoid danger.

2. The beam of light fell exactly, or _____, where he aimed it.

3. One kind of bird eats dead animals. It is a _____.

4. A person with a _____ illness is facing death.

B. Answer the following questions and give a reason for each.

1. Does a cautious person take a lot of chances? _____ Why or why not?

_____

2. Would a vulture make a good house pet? _____ Why or why not?

_____

3. If you have a mortal illness, is it serious? _____ Why or why not?

_____

4. Who needs to work more precisely: a surgeon or a person mowing a lawn? _____ Why?

_____

5. Does someone's mortal enemy want him or her to have good health? _____ Why or why not?

_____

6. Would you want a vulture to be looking at you in a hungry manner? _____ Why or why not?

_____

Writing Activity
In a few sentences, describe a nightmare you've had or one you imagine. Use at least one of the **Words to Know.**

Name_____

CINDER EDNA *(pages 14–25)*

Compare and Contrast

A **contrast** between two things is a difference between them. Usually when you look for contrasts, you also find similarities.

Find the names of the characters in "Cinder Edna" in the ovals below. Then read the details in the box. If a detail describes only one woman or only one man, write it in the part of the oval with that person's name. If it describes both women or both men, write it in the space where the two ovals overlap.

Likes jokes	Is a son of the king	Beautiful	Impractical
Believes in magic	Handsome	Bright	
Believes in recycling	Plays an instrument	Lives with stepsisters	
Is concerned with good looks	Not very bright	Practical	

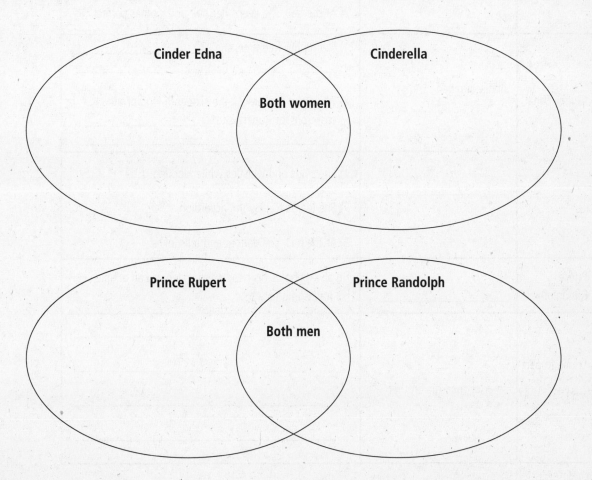

CINDER EDNA *(pages 14–25)*

Characterization

Characters are the people who take part in the action of a story. Readers learn about characters through what they say, do, and think, and through what others say about them.

Fill in any empty boxes in this chart about the characters in "Cinder Edna." Some words that describe characters are missing; some clues are incomplete.

Character	Words that describe	Clues
Cinderella	helpless	1) Before the ball, she wishes _____ 2) After the ball, she _____ _____
	_____	1) She asks for a beautiful gown. 2) At the ball, she keeps her hair and clothes perfect.
Cinder Edna	undiscouraged	1) During her free time, she _____ _____ 2) When she can't recall the sixteenth kind of tuna casserole for Rupert, she _____ _____
	_____	1) She sings and whistles while working. 2) She learns to play the accordion. 3) At the ball, she dances and tells jokes.
Prince Randolph	_____	He always holds his head so that people can admire his handsome face.
Prince Rupert	smarter than his brother	1) _____ _____ 2) _____ _____

Idioms

Idioms are phrases that mean something different from what you might think the words should mean. To understand an idiom, you must get clues from its **context,** the surrounding words or phrases.

A. Use context clues to figure out what each of the underlined idioms means. Circle the correct meaning.

1. Cinder Edna and Prince Rupert <u>cottoned to</u> each other instantly. It was as if they had been best friends their whole lives.
   a. surprised   b. liked

2. Randolph <u>didn't know beans</u> about recycling. Rupert, on the other, knew a great deal about it.
   a. knew everything   b. knew nothing

3. <u>To break the ice</u>, Cinder Edna asked Randolph what being a prince was like.
   a. to get a conversation started   b. to make the punch more drinkable

4. Prince Randolph knew that when he put his plan into action, finding his love was <u>in the bag</u>.
   a. sure to happen   b. hopeless

B. Each sentence below has an underlined idiom. Find its meaning in the right-hand column. Write the letter of the meaning in the blank.

1. _____ When Liz broke her mother's favorite vase, she was <u>in hot water</u>.

         a. unable to make up his or her mind

2. _____ Julio is usually an excellent student, but spelling is his <u>Achilles' heel</u>.

         b. in trouble

         c. important person

3. _____ That actor thinks he's a <u>big shot</u>.

         d. weak spot

4. _____ Doris can never make up her mind. Now she's <u>blowing hot and cold</u> about taking that job.

CINDER EDNA *(pages 14–25)*

Words to Know

cinders   spunky   profile   elegant   dainty

A. Use the words above and the clues below to
fill in the puzzle. Some words are already filled in.

ACROSS

1. having courage

3. ashes

5. classy

DOWN

2. view of a face from one side

4. delicate

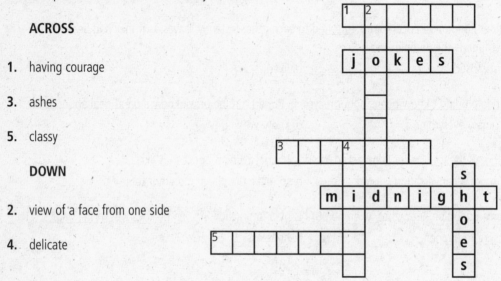

B. Choose the word or phrase that means the same as the **boldfaced** word in each sentence. Use the
dictionary if you need to.

1. Sitting in **cinders** can make you very dusty and dirty.
   a. food   b. ashes   c. water

2. The woman entered the ball dressed in a velvet gown; she looked very **elegant.**
   a. ugly   b. tired   c. classy

3. Some people have interesting features that make their **profile** easy to recognize.
   a. side view of face   b. style   c. voice

4. I would describe myself as being loud and **spunky.**
   a. shy   b. nice   c. spirited

5. The lacy tablecloth and matching napkins were quite **dainty.**
   a. dirty   b. tough   c. delicate

Writing Activity

Imagine you are a character in a fairy tale. Write three or more sentences about yourself as this character. Use
at least three of the **Words to Know.**

Name_____

THE NO-GUITAR BLUES *(pages 26–37)*

Cause and Effect

The **cause** is why something happens. The **effect** is what happens as a result. One effect may be the cause of yet another effect.

Write the missing causes and effects from "The No-Guitar Blues." Use the phrases from the box below and from the Effects column. An effect may be written again as the next cause.

the dog's owners were kind to him	he wanted a guitar
he lied about finding the dog far from its home	they gave him an old guitarron

Causes	Effects
Because Fausto wanted to be a rock star,	_____ _____
Because _____ _____	he had to get some money.
Because _____ _____	he went out looking for a job raking leaves.
Because he didn't find a job but did find a dog,	_____ _____ _____
Because _____ _____ _____	he felt guilty taking money for finding the dog.
Because _____ _____	he donated his money to the church collection.
Because Fausto's mother and grandfather wanted to help him,	_____ _____

THE NO-GUITAR BLUES *(pages 26–37)*

Conflict

Almost every story is about a problem or struggle, called a **conflict.** A single story may involve several conflicts. **External conflicts** take place between characters or between a character and nature. **Internal conflicts** take place inside a character's mind.

Each paragraph below describes some part of a problem that Fausto faces in "The No-Guitar Blues." Which type of conflict is involved? Circle the answer.

1. Fausto turned off the television set and walked outside, wondering how he could get enough money to buy a guitar.

   external conflict   internal conflict

2. Fausto decided to mow lawns to earn money, and was pushing the mower down the street before he realized it was winter and no one would hire him.

   external conflict   internal conflict

3. He would say he had found Roger near the freeway. That would scare the daylights out of the owners, who would be so happy that they would probably give him a reward. He felt bad about lying, but the dog was loose.

   external conflict   internal conflict

4. Fausto looked at the bill and knew he was in trouble. Not with these nice folks or with his parents but with himself. How could he have been so deceitful?

   external conflict   internal conflict

5. When Father Jerry began by saying that we are all sinners, Fausto thought he looked right at him. Could he know?

   external conflict   internal conflict

6. Instead of asking for the guitar, he waited for his mother to offer it to him. And she did, while gathering the dishes from the table.

   external conflict   internal conflict

THE NO-GUITAR BLUES *(pages 26–37)*

Context Clues: General

Readers can find **context clues** to the meaning of a new word by looking at the words and phrases around the word. Sometimes clues must be gathered from several passages.

A. Use context clues to find the meaning of the **boldfaced** word. Then circle the letter of each correct answer.

> "Sir," Fausto said, gripping Roger by the collar. "I found your dog by the freeway. . . . "
> Fausto looked at the bill and knew he was in trouble. Not with these nice folks or with his parents but with himself. How could he have been so deceitful? The dog wasn't lost. It was just having a fun Saturday walking around.

1. What does **deceitful** mean?
   a. helpful   b. untruthful   c. cruel

> Fausto stashed the rake and his sister's bike behind a bush. . . .
> He returned to the bush where he had hidden the rake and his sister's bike and rode home slowly. . . .

2. What does **stash** mean?
   a. break   b. join   c. hide

> He returned inside and watched his mother make tortillas. . . .
> She looked up from rolling tortillas. . . .
> Fausto walked back outside with a buttered tortilla. . . .
> A pile of tortillas lay warm under a dishtowel.

3. What does **tortilla** mean?
   a. a kind of pie   b. a kind of soup   c. a flat bread

B. Use context clues to figure out the meaning of the **boldfaced** word. Then write the answer on each blank line.

1. He saw that it was sort of a fancy dog, a terrier or something, with dog tags and a shiny collar.

   A **terrier** is _____.

2. But that night during dinner, his mother said she remembered seeing an old bass guitarron the last time she cleaned out her father's garage. . . . That was the same kind the guy in Los Lobos played.

   A **guitarron** is _____.

THE NO-GUITAR BLUES *(pages 26–37)*

Words to Know

deceitful   distracted   mission   secondhand   turnover

A. Use the **Words to Know** above to fill in the blanks. Then use the boxed letters to complete Part B.

1. This is how someone acts who does
    not want to be caught in the wrong.
    □_ _ _ _ _ _ _ _

2. This is something that you decide will be
    your goal.
    _ _ _ _ _ □_

3. To save money, Danielle
    bought used CDs at this kind of store.
    _ _ _ _ □_ _ _ _ _

4. Neil loves to eat this tasty pastry.
    _ _ _ _ _ _ □_

5. While doing your homework, you start to
    sing along with the radio. You are this.
    _ _ _ □_ _ _ _ _

6. If you decide to travel to the moon, you are going
    on this.
    _ _ _ _ _ □_

7. I was being this when I told my mother I took
    out the garbage and it was really under the sink.
    □_ _ _ _ _ _ _ _

8. Carlos liked his food warm and thought
    James was strange because he ate this cold.
    _ _ _ □_ _ _ _

9. You receive this kind of clothing when an older
    sister or brother can no longer wear it.
    _ _ _ □_ _ _ _ _

10. If you are watching a movie and turn away
    because you hear a dog barking, you are this.
    _ _ _ □_ _ _ _ _

B. Answer the question with the word the boxed letters spell out.

How does Fausto begin to find work?

He went □□□□-□□-□□□□.

Name_____

A SLAVE *(pages 40–47)*

Chronological Order

Usually events in a story are told in **chronological order,** or the order they happened. In "A Slave," some of the events are described out of sequence. That is, their order in the story does not match the order in which they happened.

When did each event listed below happen? Write each event in the correct square on the chart. The first one has been done for you.

Tice Davids runs away from the plantation.

News of friends who will help running-aways reaches the slaves.

The slave owner talks to people in Ripley, Ohio.

Ministers from the south move to Ohio.

Tice Davids swims across the Ohio River.

Tice settles in Sandusky, Ohio.

Tice disappears on the shore.

Tice is told to look for the lantern and listen for the bell.

Before Tice's escape	During Tice's escape	After Tice's escape
Ministers from the south move to Ohio.		
		The system of helping slaves is named the Underground Railroad.

A SLAVE (pages 40–47)

Literary Nonfiction

Literary nonfiction tells about real people and events. It is based on fact but includes some words and scenes that are made up by the writer.

A. Each sentence below describes a scene in "A Slave." Decide if it tells something that can probably be found in records or something made up by the writer. Put a check in the correct column.

	Fact from records	Made up by writer
1. Tice Davids escapes to freedom by crossing the Ohio River.	_____	_____
2. Some people wait at the riverbank, looking for runaway slaves that need help.	_____	_____
3. As Tice runs to freedom, he repeats the words "Look for the lantern! Listen for the bell!"	_____	_____
4. The slave owner says, "I saw him before my eyes and now he's gone."	_____	_____
5. Tice Davids makes his way to Sandusky, Ohio, and lives there as a free man.	_____	_____
6. The road for runaway slaves becomes known as the Underground Railroad.	_____	_____

B. In each pair of sentences below, only one sentence is true of literary nonfiction. Put a check mark [✔] in front of that sentence. Then cross out the words *literary nonfiction* in the incorrect sentence. Above the crossed-out words, write another kind of writing that will make the sentence true.

1. _____ Literary nonfiction is based on fact.

   _____ Literary nonfiction is based on make-believe.

2. _____ To write literary nonfiction a writer must use a lot of imagination.

   _____ To write literary nonfiction a writer must do a lot of research.

A SLAVE *(pages 40–47)*

Prefixes

A **prefix** is a word part added to the beginning of a base word. Some common prefixes are *un-*, which means "not," *re-*, which means "again," and *dis-*, which means "not" or "the opposite of."

A. Add the prefix to the base word. Write the new word on the line. Then write its meaning.

1. un- + successful = _____

   Meaning: _____

2. re- + capture = _____

   Meaning: _____

3. dis- + appear = _____

   Meaning: _____

4. re- + named = _____

   Meaning: _____

5. un- + able = _____

   Meaning: _____

6. dis- + belief = _____

   Meaning: _____

B. Choose the correct word from Exercise A to complete each sentence.

1. Tice Davids realized he was _____ to bear being a slave any longer.

2. Tice was afraid that he would be caught and his escape attempt would be

   _____.

3. He knew the slave owner would chase him and try to _____ him.

4. The slave owner was amazed to see Tice _____ after the slave had staggered onto the shore.

5. Shaking his head in _____, the slave owner said Tice must have taken an underground road.

6. Later, the underground road was _____ the Underground Railroad.

A SLAVE *(pages 40–47)*

Words to Know

plantation   revived   settlement   rails

A. Fill in the blanks with the word from the list that best completes the sentence.

1. In the South, we visited a historic _____ where cotton was grown.

2. After taking an afternoon nap, I was completely _____.

3. The Plymouth Rock colony is an example of a _____.

4. Don't walk on the _____ if you hear a train coming.

B. Write **true** or **false** in the blanks.

_____ **1.** If you cannot breathe and someone saves you, you have been revived.

_____ **2.** Farmers live on plantations in major cities.

_____ **3.** Most people drive their cars on rails.

_____ **4.** Each of today's modern cities probably started as a settlement.

_____ **5.** If a goldfish dies, you can revive it.

_____ **6.** At one time, slaves worked on plantations.

C. **Using the Dictionary: Multiple Meanings**

Many words have more than one meaning. Look up **rails** and **settlement** in a dictionary.
Use two definitions of each of the words in separate sentences. You should have four sentences.

_____

_____

_____

_____

WILMA MANKILLER *(pages 48–59)*

Making Judgments

Characters in stories may do or say things you approve of. Or they may do or say things you don't think they should. When you decide whether or not you agree with a character's actions and words, you are **making a judgment.**

For each statement about the characters in "Wilma Mankiller," circle whether you agree or disagree. Then give a reason for your answer.

1. Wilma is a good citizen.

I (agree, disagree) with this statement because _____

_____

2. The U.S. government treated the Cherokees fairly.

I (agree, disagree) with this statement because _____

_____

3. Chief Swimmer was biased against women.

I (agree, disagree) with this statement because _____

_____

4. Wilma's parents should not have left Mankiller Flats and moved to San Francisco.

I (agree, disagree) with this statement because _____

_____

5. Some of the Cherokee people should be ashamed of the way they treated Wilma.

I (agree, disagree) with this statement because _____

_____

WILMA MANKILLER *(pages 48–59)*

Details

Details are small bits of information. By combining details, writers can give a complete picture of a person, place, thing, event, or idea.

Fill in the following concept map with details from this paragraph from "Wilma Mankiller."

> In her mind, Wilma traveled back to her grandfather's land on Mankiller Flats, in Oklahoma. Her family was happy there, living close to other Cherokee families. They had springwater to drink, woods full of deer and foxes, and a home her father had built.

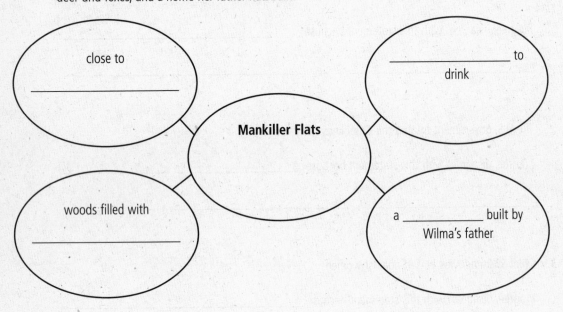

close to
_____

Mankiller Flats

_____ to
drink

woods filled with
_____

a _____ built by
Wilma's father

Now make a concept map with four details that tell what you like about your own home.

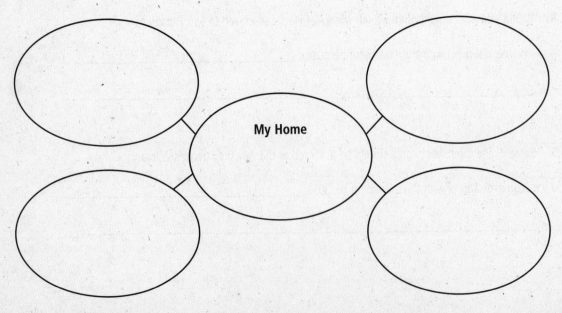

My Home

Vocabulary SkillBuilder

Name_____

WILMA MANKILLER *(pages 48–59)*

Idioms

When you hear the phrases "pulling the wool over your eyes" and "wild-goose chase," you are hearing idioms. An **idiom** is a phrase that has a meaning that is different from the surface meaning of the words. To understand an idiom, pay attention to context clues.

A. Use context clues to figure out what each of the underlined idioms means. Circle the letter beside the correct meaning.

1. Wilma Mankiller tried to <u>be of good mind</u> even though her job was hard.
   a. remember the names of anyone who had opposed her
   b. think of good things and avoid thinking of bad things

2. Wilma found herself <u>in hot water</u> when she ran for deputy chief against the wishes of many of the Cherokee people.
   a. in trouble   b. confused

3. Cherokee voters were not <u>buying a pig in a poke</u> when they elected Wilma. She had been a member of their community for years.
   a. being cruel   b. choosing without having enough information

4. Wilma was tired of letting the government <u>pull the wool over her people's eyes</u>. She wanted some truthful answers.
   a. take her people's sheep   b. fool her people

B. Each sentence below has an underlined idiom. Find its meaning in the right-hand column. Write the letter of the meaning beside the sentence.

_____ 1. I slept <u>like a top</u> last night. I feel great.

_____ 2. Blake caught the bus <u>by the skin of his teeth</u>. He was glad the driver waited for him.

_____ 3. I haven't seen my cousin in <u>a month of Sundays</u>.

_____ 4. You sent me on a <u>wild-goose chase</u>. I couldn't find what I was looking for in your closet.

a. just barely

b. worthless errand

c. well

d. a long time

WILMA MANKILLER *(pages 48–59)*

Words to Know

coyotes   bugles   council   swirling

A. Fill in each blank with the word from the list that best completes the sentence.

1. The _____ are played every morning to wake up the soldiers.

2. I woke up to find the snow _____ in the storm outside of

   my window.

3. The _____ howled in the distance, scaring the baby.

4. The city _____ met to discuss the new park that was

   being set up downtown.

B. Circle the letter next to the word that doesn't belong. Use a dictionary, if necessary.

1. a. trumpets   b. bugles   c. coins

2. a. council   b. zoo   c. tribe

3. a. sleeping   b. swirling   c. twisting

4. a. wolves   b. sheep   c. coyotes

Writing Activity
Imagine you are running for mayor. Write the beginning of a speech you would give to convince people that you would be a good choice. Use at least one of the **Words to Know.**

CESAR CHAVEZ: CIVIL-RIGHTS CHAMPION *(pages 60–67)*

Fact and Opinion

A **fact** is a statement that is known to be true. An **opinion** is a personal belief or feeling. A fact can be proved by public records, but an opinion cannot be proved.

Read each of these items about "Cesar Chavez: Civil-Rights Champion" and decide whether it is a fact or an opinion. Write **fact** or **opinion** on the line. Then write the number of the item in the correct box in the charts below.

_____ **1.** Cesar Chavez is the most important civil-rights leader of the 20th century.

_____ **2.** All civil-rights leaders should fast the way Chavez did.

_____ **3.** Chavez began the National Farm Workers Association.

_____ **4.** It is wrong for workers to strike for better pay.

_____ **5.** If working conditions do not improve, more grape boycotts may take place.

_____ **6.** In the future, migrant workers will demand better working conditions.

_____ **7.** Farmers should build better labor camps for migrant workers.

_____ **8.** Many civil-rights groups and churches supported Chavez in his struggle on behalf of migrant workers.

Facts	Opinions		
	I know these items are opinions because		
I know these are facts because there are proofs in public records: _____ and _____	(a) the sentence uses a word like *good* or *bad:* _____ and _____	(b) the sentence uses a word like *may* or *will:* _____ and _____	(c) the sentence uses a word like *should* or *must:* _____ and _____

CESAR CHAVEZ: CIVIL-RIGHTS CHAMPION *(pages 60–67)*

Biography

A **biography** tells the life story of a real person. It explains why the person is important. The writer tells facts about the person's life, usually in the order in which they happened.

A. Circle the correct answer to each question about "Cesar Chavez: Civil-Rights Champion."

    1. Who tells the story of Cesar Chavez's life?

        a. Chavez himself   b. another writer

    2. Where did the writer get information and ideas for this article?

        a. his or her own imagination   b. factual accounts (newspapers, city records, etc.)

    3. How are most of the facts in "Cesar Chavez" organized?

        a. order of importance   b. time order

B. The following facts recall events from "Cesar Chavez: Civil-Rights Champion." Write the number of each event in the correct place on the time line below. One item has been done for you.

    1. is born in Yuma, Arizona.

    2. fasts to protest use of pesticides

    3. forms the National Farm Workers Association

    4. family loses farm and all become migrant workers

    5. Ten thousand people march on the state capital in Sacramento in support of the grape pickers' strike.

    6. dies in California

    7. fasts to protest right-to-work laws

    8. serves in the Navy during World War II

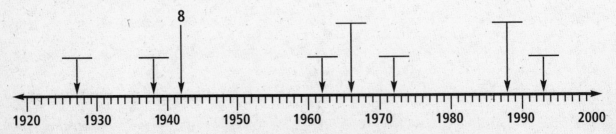

CESAR CHAVEZ: CIVIL-RIGHTS CHAMPION *(pages 60–67)*

Context Clues: Definition

A clue to the meaning of a difficult word is often found in **context,** that is, the sentence or paragraph where the word appears. A **definition clue** states the meaning of a new word.

A. Find a definition of the underlined word in the context. Write the meaning on the line.

1. Many grape pickers are <u>migrants</u>. They are workers who travel from place to place picking crops.

   Migrants are _____.

2. Union <u>negotiators</u>, who are people who discuss issues and help make agreements, talked with the grape growers.

   Negotiators are _____.

3. Crops often are sprayed with <u>pesticides</u>, which are chemicals used to kill insects.

   Pesticides are _____.

4. Chavez helped Mexican Americans <u>register</u> to vote. In other words, they signed an official voter list.

   To register means to _____.

5. After years of strikes and fasting, Chavez and his union <u>prevailed</u>, that is, they won the victory.

   To prevail means to _____.

B. Choose one of the words below to complete each sentence.

negotiators   migrants   prevail

1. The people who talk and try to make agreements, that is, the _____, worked very hard during the lettuce boycott.

2. Cesar Chavez proved that by using nonviolent protest the union would _____. In other words, through this method it would win the victory.

3. Farmworkers often travel from place to place to find work. They are

   _____.

CESAR CHAVEZ: CIVIL-RIGHTS CHAMPION *(pages 60–67)*

Words to Know

nonviolent   union   motto   tactics   fasts

A. Fill in the blanks with the word from the list that best completes the sentence.

1. Each of the men running for president had some plans, or
_____, to get votes.

2. A _____ protects the rights of workers.

3. I believe in peaceful change, and therefore I'm _____.

4. "Work hard, play hard" is our _____.

5. To protest unfair laws the workers refused to eat and went on _____.

B. Locate the **Words to Know** in the Word Search below. Then match each with its definition.

q	n	x	j	y	h	d	g	b	m	m	p
m	k	h	u	z	e	x	a	w	p	o	n
a	n	o	n	v	i	o	l	e	n	t	a
l	b	s	i	f	c	f	a	s	t	s	
r	c	i	o	w	o	u	j	v	v	o	f
t	b	s	n	t	y	d	o	k	u	q	e
r	t	n	c	g	t	a	c	t	i	c	s

1. not using force _____

2. periods of time without food _____

3. methods used to get results _____

4. organized group of workers _____

5. sentence that states group goals _____

Writing Activity
Work with a group of students to create a motto that fits your group. Read it aloud to the rest of the class. Use at least one of the **Words to Know.**

ROBERTO CLEMENTE: HERO AND FRIEND (pages 68–77)

Chronological Order

Usually in a biography, a writer presents events of a person's life in the order in which they happened. This order is called **chronological** or **time order.**

Some details from "Roberto Clemente: Hero and Friend" are listed in chronological order on the chart below. Complete the order of events on the chart. Use details from the bottom of the page.

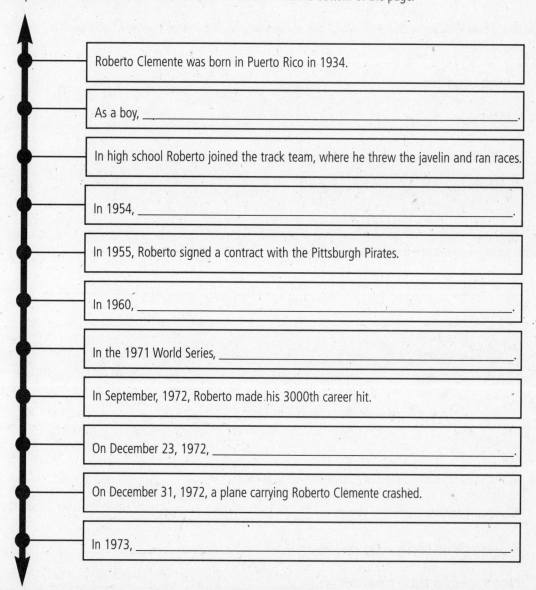

Roberto Clemente was born in Puerto Rico in 1934.

As a boy, _____.

In high school Roberto joined the track team, where he threw the javelin and ran races.

In 1954, _____.

In 1955, Roberto signed a contract with the Pittsburgh Pirates.

In 1960, _____.

In the 1971 World Series, _____.

In September, 1972, Roberto made his 3000th career hit.

On December 23, 1972, _____.

On December 31, 1972, a plane carrying Roberto Clemente crashed.

In 1973, _____.

---

an earthquake struck Nicaragua.

Roberto became the first Hispanic voted into the Hall of Fame.

Roberto batted .414.

Roberto led the Pirates to the World Series.

Roberto joined the farm team of the Brooklyn Dodgers.

Roberto used sticks and cans to play baseball.

ROBERTO CLEMENTE: HERO AND FRIEND *(pages 68–77)*

Reading for Details (SQ3R)

Often you read nonfiction to learn and remember facts. A way to study and remember what you read is the SQ3R method. **SQ3R** stands for **Survey** (look over), **Question** (ask what you want to learn from the nonfiction), **Read, Record** (take notes), and **Review.**

Use the SQ3R method to study "Roberto Clemente: Hero and Friend." Follow these directions.

Survey Take a brief look at the selection. Which one of the following features do you see? Circle that choice.

    a. charts and graphs

    b. photographs

    c. headings

    d. subheadings

Question Write two questions that most people would have about Roberto Clemente.

_____

_____

Read Read (or reread) "Roberto Clemente: Hero and Friend." Before you start, write your beginning time here:

_____. When you finish, write your ending time here: _____.

Record Without looking back at the story, answer these questions.

    1. Where was Roberto born? _____

    2. For which city did he play as a major league ball player? _____

    3. What is one other fact in the article? _____

Review Find answers to the questions in the article. Place a check mark next to each fact you remembered correctly.

ROBERTO CLEMENTE: HERO AND FRIEND *(pages 68–77)*

Specialized Vocabulary

Every job, sport, hobby, or other activity has its own special words or special meanings for common words. Context clues help you understand these words.

Each underlined word is used in two different ways. Read each sentence carefully. Then use context clues to choose the meaning that makes the most sense. Write the correct letter in front of each sentence.

1. _____ That seat is uncomfortable because it is in a <u>draft</u>.

   _____ The Pittsburgh Pirates claimed Roberto in the <u>draft</u>.

   a. in major league sports, a system for teams to obtain players
   b. a breeze

2. _____ The outfielder's splendid <u>catch</u> robbed the batter of a hit.

   _____ The frightened child spoke clearly, but there was a <u>catch</u> in his voice.

   a. in baseball and other sports, the act of taking hold of a ball in flight
   b. a break in the voice, caused by strong feeling

3. _____ We store the <u>bats</u> in this locker.

   _____ Hundreds of <u>bats</u> flew from the cave at dusk.

   a. in science, a type of flying mammal
   b. in baseball, a club used to strike at the ball

4. _____ Usually, <u>stepping</u> into the bucket hampers a smooth swing.

   _____ I got an injured foot from <u>stepping</u> into the bucket of nails.

   a. in baseball, moving the front foot way from home plate when batting
   b. putting the foot down

5. _____ The runner slid into the <u>plate</u> safely.

   _____ Be sure to eat everything on your <u>plate</u>.

   a. a shallow dish
   b. in baseball, a short version of home plate, the five-sided slab that a base runner must cross in order to score

ROBERTO CLEMENTE: HERO AND FRIEND *(pages 68–77)*

Words to Know

determined   prospects   prejudice   potential

A. Circle the letter of the word or phrase that is most similar to the **boldfaced** word. Use the dictionary, if you need to.

1. Jan knew many other **prospects** were interviewing for the job.

   a. people with possibilities   b. young mothers   c. lawyers

2. Lawrence got involved with groups that tried to get rid of **prejudice.**

   a. insects   b. unfair treatment   c. pollution

3. I am **determined** to win this leg of the race.

   a. very scared   b. firmly decided   c. against

4. My chorus instructor said I had the **potential** to become an amazing singer.

   a. vocal cords   b. grades   c. ability

B. Answer each question by filling in a word from the list at the top.

1. What could you call a group of possible friends? _____

2. If someone tries as hard as she can to get something, what is she? _____

3. If you don't do your best, you aren't living up to your what? _____

4. What word describes an attitude against people of color? _____

Writing Activity

Imagine that you are a sports star. What is your sport? What position do you play? Write at least three sentences about your life as a famous figure, using at least one of the **Words to Know.**

TROMBONES AND COLLEGES *(pages 80–89)*

Making Inferences

Inferences are logical guesses that readers make about why characters in a story act as they do and what story events mean. Readers make inferences by combining evidence from the story with their own experience.

Read each passage about the characters and events in the story "Trombones and Colleges." For each passage, underline the inference that makes the most sense.

1. Clyde says that his adviser had told him to switch back to the commercial program. He looks like he'll start crying any minute. His eyes are red, and his voice is shaky.
   What can you infer about Clyde's feelings from his words and actions?

   a. Clyde is pleased that he can switch back to the commercial program.

   b. Clyde is unhappy with the idea of switching back to the commercial program.

   c. Clyde is nervous about switching back to the commercial program.

2. When Mrs. Jones comes into the kitchen, she notices that the young people suddenly stop talking. She tells them not to worry—that she will leave them alone as soon as she puts the food away.
   What can you infer about Mrs. Jones from her words?

   a. Mrs. Jones knows that young people need their privacy at times.

   b. Mrs. Jones always wants to know exactly what her children are doing and saying.

   c. Mrs. Jones doesn't really care much about her children.

3. After Mrs. Jones sees Clyde's poor report card and hears what the adviser has told Clyde to do, she looks at him and asks him what he is going to do.
   What can you infer about the relationship between Clyde and his mother from her reaction?

   a. Clyde's mother always makes his decisions for him because she knows that he can't be trusted to do the right thing.

   b. Clyde's mother is often disappointed in her son and never expects him to do well.

   c. Clyde's mother treats her son with respect.

4. Clyde decides that he will stay in the academic program even though it is hard.
   What can you infer about Clyde from this decision?

   a. Clyde sometimes makes foolish decisions.

   b. Clyde doesn't give up easily when he really wants something.

   c. Clyde loves to work hard at everything.

TROMBONES AND COLLEGES *(pages 80–89)*

Theme

The **theme** of a story is the lesson about life or human nature that it teaches.

Read this list of themes. For each event from "Trombones and Colleges," choose a theme that the event teaches or reminds you of. Write it in the box. Make up a theme to match the last event.

Themes

If you work hard, you can do almost anything you want to do.

Love and support from your family can make you feel better when times are hard.

Good friends don't hurt each other's feelings.

Story Event	Theme or Lesson Taught
The narrator is careful not to tell Clyde that his own report card was good when he sees how bad Clyde feels.	_____
Clyde's father always set his goals high and never stopped trying, even when people said he wasn't good enough.	_____
Clyde feels better when his mother lets him know that she is glad that he will keep trying the academic program.	_____
Clyde and his friends decide that they will all study together sometimes.	_____

TROMBONES AND COLLEGES *(pages 80–89)*

Context Clues

To figure out the meaning of a word, look for **context clues** in the words and phrases around the word.

A. Use context clues to figure out the meaning of the **boldfaced** word.

1. Clyde had **satisfactory** marks in Personal Traits and Behavior, but his marks for math and history were terrible.

   Satisfactory means _____

2. Mathematics was a **required,** or necessary, subject in the academic program.

   Required means _____

3. Mrs. Jones rinsed the rice in a **colander,** and she watched the water stream out the holes into the sink.

   A **colander** is _____

4. Clyde's parents lived in a **rooming house,** a place where people rent rooms.

   A **rooming house** is _____

5. Clyde's father tried to look **nonchalant,** not as eager and excited as he was really feeling.

   Nonchalant means _____

B. Use the correct word to complete each sentence.

     satisfactory   required   nonchalant

1. It's hard to act _____ when you are looking at a big, red F on your report card.

2. Even when Alison gets a B, her parents tell her that her grades are not

   _____ and she should try harder.

3. Taking three years of English is _____ if you want to enter that college.

TROMBONES AND COLLEGES *(pages 80–89)*

Words to Know

system   required   annoyed   document   disgusted

A. Fill in each blank with one of the **Words to Know.**

1. Sam and his mother had a _____ for doing laundry.

2. Clyde's report card looked like a very important _____.

3. Clyde became _____ when his sister continued to bother him.

4. When Clyde's father couldn't play the trombone, he became irritated and impatient, or

   _____.

5. Some classes are _____, or needed, to graduate.

B. Match each word with a definition. Write the letter of the correct definition on the blank.

_____ **1.** system   a. needed

_____ **2.** document   b. irritated and impatient

_____ **3.** required   c. set way of doing things

_____ **4.** disgusted   d. bothered

_____ **5.** annoyed   e. official report

Writing Activity

Suppose your friend received a bad report card. Write three sentences to make excuses for him or her. Use at least two of the **Words to Know.**

IN A NEIGHBORHOOD IN LOS ANGELES (pages 90–93)

Speaker

The **speaker** in a poem or a story is the voice who is speaking to the reader. The writer uses that character's voice.

A.   Read each passage. Identify the character who is speaking.

1.   I remember the day Anna was born like it was yesterday. I went to the hospital with a toy for the baby. My daughter lay in bed looking happy and proud. My son-in-law took me to the nursery to see Anna. I loved her from the moment I saw her.

   The speaker is _____.

2.   I have a great life. Every day, I sit on a rock in the pond and warm myself in the sun. When I get hungry, I slide into the water and look for a snack. Whenever I feel afraid, I pull my head, arms, and legs into my shell.

   The speaker is _____.

3.   It's a sunny day, so I know people will visit me. I'll just sit here and wait in the park by the footpath. Mothers will sit on me while they watch their children play. Bird lovers will rest on me while they feed the birds. I'm starting to look a little rundown. I wonder if I will get painted today.

   The speaker is _____.

4.   I'm afraid when Mommy turns the lights off. I hope there are no monsters under my bed. What is that sound? Is it coming from my closet? I'm glad that Mommy came back and turned that little light on.

   The speaker is _____.

B.   Try to remember what it was like to be a young child in your home on a holiday. Write two or three sentences in which the speaker is you when you were about seven years old. Be sure to use the word *I* in your sentences.

_____

_____

_____

MUDSLINGING (pages 94–97)

Summarizing

In a **summary,** you write the important ideas from a text in a shortened form and in your own words.

Read each passage from "Mudslinging." Then circle the letter of the better summary.

1. The day before the wedding, the groom's father visits the bride's house. He knocks on the door and insists on being let in. With him are other members of the groom's family: aunts and uncles, sisters and brothers.

   Those inside the house open the door just a crack and say, "Who are you? What do you want?" They act like they don't know him. "War is declared!" the groom's father announces loudly. He pushes the door open, and then the craziness begins.

   a. The groom's father, along with the rest of the groom's family—aunts, uncles, sisters, and brothers—visits the bride's house, and the craziness begins.

   b. The groom's father visits the bride's house and demands to be let in. The bride's family pretend they don't know him, and the war begins.

2. The groom and his family have secretly prepared buckets of mud, which they have brought with them. The mud is four different colors, one for each of the four directions: north, south, east, and west. It is sacred mud. These people rush into the bride's house and grab everyone, including the bride, and drag them out into the yard. The groom's family dig into the buckets of mud and begin throwing it, smearing it on every person they can catch. The bride's family dip into the mud, too. Before long the yard is swarming with people of all ages, from babies to old grandmothers and grandfathers, flinging mud at each other as if they've lost their minds.

   a. The groom and his family bring buckets of mud. After they pull everyone from the bride's house outside, they begin to throw mud at the bride and her family. The bride's family starts throwing mud from the buckets at the groom's family. Soon everyone is throwing mud.

   b. The groom's family brings pails of mud. The mud is sacred. It is four different colors for the four directions: the north, the south, the east, and the west.

3. The Mudslinging ends peacefully. Once the buckets are emptied and everyone is coated with mud, the participants shake hands and make peace. Food is shared, a feast of corn and mutton, a lot of food.

   a. The Mudslinging ends peacefully. The participants shake hands and make peace.

   b. After the Mudslinging ends, everyone makes peace and shares a feast.

MUDSLINGING *(pages 94–97)*

Author's Purpose

The reason why an author writes is called the **author's purpose.**

Read each passage below. Then fill in the chart with the author's purpose. Choose from these purposes:

to teach or inform

to entertain

to persuade the reader to think or act in a certain way

to share thoughts and feelings

Passage	Author's Purpose
1. Be sure to come to our beautiful city on your next trip. While you are here, you can see works of art in our museums. You can see a play or visit the world-famous zoo. If you want to know more about the fun you can have here, look at our Web site today. Don't wait. Act now!	_____ _____ _____
2. Riddle: What do you give an alligator that demands dinner? Answer: Anything it wants	_____ _____ _____
3. The Mudslinging ends peacefully. Once the buckets are emptied and everyone is coated with mud, the participants shake hands and make peace. Food is shared, a feast of corn and mutton, a lot of food.	_____ _____ _____
4. I love the country after a snowstorm. To me, the tree branches covered with snow look like something from a fairy tale. The sunlight on the new snow almost blinds me with its clean whiteness. If I ever moved away from my snowy home, I'd make sure that, at least once every winter, I could visit it just after a big snowfall.	_____ _____ _____

MUDSLINGING *(pages 94–97)*

Synonyms

A **synonym** is a word that means the same, or nearly the same, as another word. For example, *bucket* and *pail* are synonyms.

A. Circle the word that is a synonym for the underlined word in each sentence.

1. Can you imagine families <u>throwing</u> mud, just for fun?

   hurling　　　　　　making　　　　　　bringing

2. Believe it or not, there is a <u>purpose</u> for the custom.

   punishment　　　　　price　　　　　　reason

3. Marriage is a <u>solemn</u> event to the Hopi people.

   old-fashioned　　　　serious　　　　　silly

4. Mudslinging happens the day before the <u>wedding</u> takes place.

   marriage　　　　　　fight　　　　　　insult

5. The groom's father visits the <u>home</u> of the bride's family.

   church　　　　　　house　　　　　　father

6. He <u>knocks</u> at the bride's door.

   kneels　　　　　　waits　　　　　　raps

7. The groom's family has <u>brought</u> buckets of mud to throw at the bride's family.

   forgotten　　　　　carried　　　　　made

B. Match each word to its synonym. On each blank, write the letter of the correct synonym.

　_____ **1.** drag　　　a. grownup

　_____ **2.** foolish　　b. holy

　_____ **3.** adult　　　c. village

　_____ **4.** sacred　　d. pull

　_____ **5.** town　　　e. silly

MUDSLINGING (pages 94–97)

Words to Know

custom   sacred   wistful   disputes   hilarity

A. Fill in each blank with the word from the list that best completes the sentence.

1. Mudslinging is a Hopi _____ that is done when people get married.

2. Dan's face became _____ as he remembered his wedding day.

3. Sometimes family members have arguments, or _____.

4. Mudslinging is a time of much fun and _____.

5. The Hopi use four kinds of _____ mud for the Mudslinging.

B. Write **true** or **false** in each blank.

_____ 1. A **custom** is a bucket filled with mud.

_____ 2. Something that is **sacred** is the same as something that is holy.

_____ 3. A **wistful** expression is dreamy.

_____ 4. **Hilarity** means names people call each other.

_____ 5. Saying mean things to someone can cause **disputes**.

Writing Activity

An **acrostic** is a poem or series of lines in which the beginning letters form a message or name. Look at the word "mud" as shown below. Next to each letter, use the **Words to Know** to write a sentence about the Hopi marriage ritual.

M _____

U _____

D _____

ANOTHER APRIL *(pages 98–112)*

Details

Details tell more about the main ideas in a paragraph.

Answer the questions below, using details from the following paragraphs.

> "He used to be a powerful man," Mom said more to herself than she did to me. "He was a timber cutter. No man could cut more timber than my father; no man in the timber woods could sink an ax deeper into a log than my father. And no man could lift the end of a bigger saw log than Pop could."

1. What had been Pop's job? _____

2. Name two tasks Pop had done well on the job. _____

   _____

> As I watched Grandpa go down the path toward the hog pen, he stopped to examine every little thing along his path. Once he waved his cane at a butterfly as it zigzagged over his head, its polka-dot wings fanning the blue April air. . . . When he reached the hog pen, he called the hogs down to the fence. . . . He leaned his cane against the hog pen, reached over the fence, and patted the hogs' heads. Grandpa didn't miss patting one of our seven hogs.

3. At what does Grandpa wave his cane? _____

4. What does Grandpa do first when he reaches the hog pen? _____

5. How does Grandpa show that he likes the hogs? _____

   _____

> But each year he didn't take as long a walk as he had taken the year before. Now this spring he didn't go down to the lower end of the hog pen as he had done last year. And when I could first remember Grandpa going on his walks, he used to go out of sight. He'd go all over the farm. And he'd come to the house and take me on his knee and tell me about all what he had seen. Now Grandpa wasn't getting out of sight. I could see him from the window along all of his walk.

6. Where did Grandpa go last year that he doesn't go now? _____

   _____

7. Where did Grandpa used to go on his walks? _____

8. What did Grandpa used to do when he came back from his walks? _____

ANOTHER APRIL *(pages 98–112)*

Setting

The **setting** of a story is when and where it takes place. In some stories, the setting is described in detail.

Read each passage from "Another April." On the sketch below, draw in the objects that Grandpa saw on his walk. Include as many details as you can.

1. Since Mom wouldn't let me go with Grandpa, I watched him as he walked slowly down the path in front of our house.

2. I watched Grandpa stop under the pine tree in our front yard.

3. As I watched Grandpa go down the path toward the hog pen, he stopped to examine every little thing along his path.

4. When he reached the hog pen, he called the hogs down to the fence.

5. As he toddled up the little path alongside the hog pen, he stopped under a blooming tree.

6. Grandpa didn't come back into the house at the front door. He toddled around back of the house toward the smokehouse.

7. We watched Grandpa as he walked down beside our smokehouse where a tall sassafras tree's thin leaves fluttered in the blue April wind.

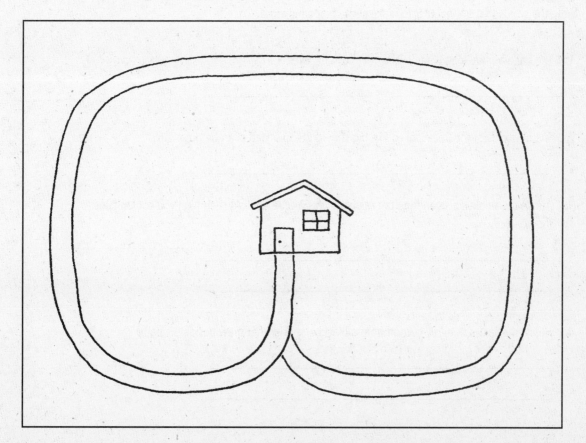

ANOTHER APRIL *(pages 98–112)*

Compound Words

A **compound word** is made by putting two words together. Sometimes the words are written as one word. Other times, the words are combined with a hyphen [-]. Sometimes the two words are written as separate words but used together.

A. Combine each word in Row 1 with a word in Row 2 to make a compound word. Complete the sentences with the compound words you make.

Row 1:   bare   over   bumble   dining   polka-
Row 2:   bee   footed   room   coat   dot

1. Grandpa watched the _____ buzz near the windflower.

2. Mom made Grandpa wear his _____ to go outside.

3. The child took off his shoes and ran _____ through the creek.

4. Grandpa waved his cane at a butterfly with _____ wings.

5. The child could see Grandpa through the window in the _____.

B. Circle the compound words in these sentences about the story "Another April." Then, under each sentence, write the words that go together to make each compound word.

1. The old man had long white eyebrows above his eyes.

    _____ + _____

2. The blossoms of the trees looked like big snowdrifts sprinkled over the green hills.

    _____ + _____

3. Above the smokehouse and the tall sassafras was a blue April sky—so high you couldn't see the sky-roof.

    _____ + _____

    _____ + _____

4. He even pulled a butterfly cocoon from a blackberry briar that grew beside his path.

    _____ + _____

    _____ + _____

ANOTHER APRIL *(pages 98–112)*

Words to Know

coarse   timber   bundled   terrapin

A. Circle the letter next to the word or phrase that is most similar to the **boldfaced** word.

1. Grandpa's hands were **coarse**—like the bark of a tree.

　　a. gentle　　　　b. soft　　　　　　c. rough

2. When it is cold, Grandpa is **bundled** in a heavy wool coat.

　　a. hidden　　　　b. wrapped up　　　c. sweating

3. The old **terrapin** lives in the pond.

　　a. rock　　　　　b. fish　　　　　　c. turtle

4. We used **timber** from the forest to build the fire.

　　a. wood　　　　　b. leaves　　　　　c. flowers

B. Fill in each blank with the word from the list that best completes the sentence.

1. The _____ walked slowly on its four legs.

2. The boy's mother _____ him in two sweaters and a coat.

3. Settlers cut _____ to make houses.

4. The rough sandpaper is _____.

Writing Activity
Write three sentences about springtime. Use at least three **Words to Know.**

THE TELEPHONE (pages 116–127)

Making Inferences

An **inference** is a logical guess that a reader makes using clues in a story.

The first column below lists clues from *The Telephone*. The second column lists inferences you can make using these clues. Fill in the blanks in both the clues and inferences.

Clue	Inference
1. Aunt Elizabeth tells Mildred that Hathaway House was once a _____ place.	_____ hasn't lived at Hathaway House for very long.
2. After _____ frightens Mildred, he just says, "What's the matter with you?"	Victor is not usually very _____ to his wife.
3. Victor hopes that Elizabeth will be so shocked when she hears the telephone ring that she will suffer a heart attack, and then he will inherit _____.	Victor is a _____ person.
4. Mildred doesn't tell _____ about Victor's cruel plan.	Mildred is too afraid of _____ to tell the truth.
5. Aunt Elizabeth tells _____, "Yes, Victor and Mildred will be there in a minute," after Victor and Mildred leave.	Elizabeth and _____ had planned the attack earlier because they knew that Victor wanted their _____.
6. Aunt Elizabeth _____ after she hears Victor's and Mildred's screams and a loud thud.	Aunt Elizabeth may have known that Victor planned to _____ her and is happy to have stopped him.

THE TELEPHONE *(pages 116–127)*

Dramatic Form

Plays are meant to be acted out. So playwrights write them in a special way so that actors and directors know exactly what to do.

Answer these questions about the play *The Telephone*.

1. Circle the names of the characters for which the director needs to find actors.

    Aunt Elizabeth   Victor   Jonathan   Mildred

2. On the line next to the character's name, write the letter of the stage directions that character needs to follow.

    _____ Mildred   ___ Aunt Elizabeth   _____ Victor

    a. (. . . *raises hand as if to strike her, just as* Aunt Elizabeth *re-enters with raincoat. Quickly . . . drops hand.*)
    b. (*Laughs in satisfied way as curtain closes.*)
    c. (*She sits on sofa, stares at phone. Suddenly phone rings. . . . screams, jumps to her feet. Phone rings again. Slowly, her hand trembling, she picks up receiver, speaks into phone.*)

3. Which of these objects, or props, are needed for the play? Circle your answers.

    raincoat   telephone   large key

4. Which of these sounds should the audience hear? Circle your answers.

    a telephone ringing   a dog barking   a woman screaming   thunder

5. Match these stage directions from *The Telephone* with their labels. Write the letter of the matching stage direction on the line.

    _____ Setting   _____ Time   _____ At Curtain Rise

    a. Mildred Hathaway *stands near French window, pulling back drapes and staring out at storm.* Aunt Elizabeth, *wearing black shawl, sits on sofa. She touches telephone, then nods to herself. There is a flash of lightning.* Mildred *jumps, then crosses hurriedly to sit beside* Elizabeth.
    b. *Drawing room of Hathaway House. Through French window, upstage, we see occasional flashes of lightning. Sounds of thunder are heard from offstage. There is a sofa down left, and a telephone on a table beside it.*
    c. *Late evening.*

THE TELEPHONE *(pages 116–127)*

Suffixes

A **suffix** is a word part added to the end of a base word.

> The suffix *-less* means "without," as in *hopeless,* meaning "without hope."
> The suffixes *-ful* and *-ous* mean "full of" or "having," as in *famous,* meaning "having fame."
> The suffix *-ly* means "in a certain way." For example, *quickly* means "in a quick way."

A. Match each word with its meaning. Write the letter of the meaning by the word.

1. _____ restless   a. having hazards

2. _____ sadly   b. without rest

3. _____ hazardous   c. full of hate

4. _____ hateful   d. in a sad way

B. Write the base word and the suffix that go together to make each word below.

1. joyous =   _____ + _____

2. noiseless =   _____ + _____

3. really =   _____ + _____

4. thoughtful =   _____ + _____

C. Underline the word with a suffix in each of these sentences. Then write the word, its base word, and the suffix on the lines.

1. The stage is dimly lit as the play begins.

_____ = _____ + _____

2. Mildred sees a mysterious figure at the window.

_____ = _____ + _____

3. Aunt Elizabeth is hopeful that Jonathan will call, even though he is dead.

_____ = _____ + _____

4. It seems pointless to try to convince Elizabeth that Jonathan will never return.

_____ = _____ + _____

THE TELEPHONE *(pages 116–127)*

Words to Know

reassuringly   stipulated   inherit   novice   menacingly

A. Fill in each blank with the word from the list that best fits the sentence.

1. The doctor _____ touched the woman's arm as he told her that her son would be fine.

2. The champion laughed as the young _____ stepped up to challenge her.

3. Until 1920, the law _____ that only men had the right to vote.

4. I will _____ my grandfather's toy train collection when he dies.

5. The pitcher looked at the batter _____ in order to scare him.

B. Match the word with its correct definition.

_____ **1.** inherit   a. beginner

_____ **2.** menacingly   b. in a way that makes one trust

_____ **3.** novice   c. in a threatening way

_____ **4.** reassuringly   d. ordered

_____ **5.** stipulated   e. receive from one who has died

Writing Activity

Write down a short telephone conversation in which a person tells you a secret. Set up your writing like a play, with your name in front of your lines, and the other person's name in front of his or hers. Use at least two **Words to Know.**

THE PRINCE AND THE PAUPER (pages 128–157)

Sequence

Events in a story or a play are usually described in the order they happen. That is, they are described in sequence.

Fill in the blanks below to complete the sequence of events from the first scene of the play *The Prince and the Pauper.*

Event 1

Tom Canty waits outside the palace to

see _____.

Event 2

The Prince invites Tom inside

_____.

Event 3

The Prince asks Tom to tell him about

_____.

Event 4

The Prince decides that he and Tom will

_____

_____.

Event 5

Before he goes, the Prince hides

_____ inside

_____.

Event 6

At the gate, a guard seizes

_____,

and the Villagers take him away.

Event 7

Tom admits to everyone that he is really

_____

_____.

Event 8

The King decides that Tom is

_____

and orders him to rest.

THE PRINCE AND THE PAUPER *(pages 128–157)*

Plot

The **plot** of a story or play is the series of events that make up the story. In the **introduction,** you meet the characters and learn the problem. The problem gets worse during the **rising action.** The **climax** is the most important event. In the **falling action and conclusion,** loose ends are tied up and the story ends.

The following sentences tell in order the events in the plot of *The Prince and the Pauper.*

    a. The Prince lets Tom into the palace.

    b. The Prince and Tom exchange clothes.

    c. A guard knocks down the Prince and tells him to leave.

    d. The King mistakes Tom for his son, the Prince.

    e. John Canty carries off the Prince.

    f. Miles and the Prince go to jail.

    g. The Prince and Tom finally get back together.

    h. The Prince proves who he really is.

Use the letters from the sentences above to answer these questions.

    1. Which two events are in the **introduction?**

_____

    2. Which four events are part of the **rising action?**

_____

    3. Which event is the **climax,** or turning point, of the story?

_____

    4. Which event is part of the **falling action and conclusion?**

_____

THE PRINCE AND THE PAUPER *(pages 128–157)*

Context Clues

Use the **context,** the words and phrases around a word, to understand its meaning.

A. Use context clues to figure out the meaning of the boldfaced word.

1. Tom Canty was a **pauper,** which is a person who is poor.

   Pauper means _____

2. The writer describes the **interior** of the palace, but not its outside.

   Interior means _____

3. The Prince looked **weary.** Because he seemed so tired, Miles felt sorry for him.

   Weary means _____

4. Tom had never before seen vegetables such as lettuce or **turnips.**

   Turnips are _____

5. After the king died, Tom was **stunned,** or shocked.

   Stunned means _____

B. Use the correct word to complete each sentence.

   interior   pauper   stunned

1. I don't want to be a _____; I'd like to be rich instead.

2. Let's look at the _____ of the home, now that we've seen the outside.

3. The news _____ me so much that I had to sit down right away.

THE PRINCE AND THE PAUPER *(pages 128–157)*

Words to Know

heir   affliction   impostor   oppress

A. Fill in each blank with the word from the list that best completes the sentence.

1. The death of Jessica's dog caused her more pain and _____ than we imagined.

2. The man pretending to be the president is an _____.

3. Jaime is an only child and the _____ to the family fortune.

4. The cruel ruler chose to _____ the people and treat them harshly.

5. Kevin's knee injury was an _____ for many years.

6. When a king dies, he leaves his title to his _____.

7. She tried to deceive everyone, but we knew that she was an _____.

8. Some laws treat people fairly, while others _____ people.

B. Homophones are words that sound alike but have different spellings and definitions. For example:

heir *(n.)* someone who gets a person's money or title after the person dies

air *(n.)* the invisible mixture of odorless, tasteless gases surrounding the earth

Place the correct homophone in the following sentences.

1. The _____ felt warm on my skin.

2. Sonia is the _____ to her parents' property.

Writing Activity

If you could switch places with anyone for a day, who would it be? Why? Write one or two sentences. Use at least one of the **Words to Know.**

DUST OF SNOW *(pages 160–161)*

Rhyme

Words **rhyme** when the sounds at the end are repeated. Poets sometimes create a pattern of rhyming words at the ends of lines. You can trace the pattern by assigning letters of the alphabet to each line, beginning with the letter *a*. Assign the same letter to lines that rhyme. Look at the excerpt from the poem "Paul Revere's Ride" and notice the pattern.

Listen, my children, and you shall hear	*a*
Of the midnight ride of Paul Revere,	*a*←(*a* again because *Revere* rhymes with *hear*)
On the eighteenth of April, in Seventy-five;	*b*
Hardly a man is now alive	*b*
Who remembers that famous day and year.	*a*

—Henry Wadsworth Longfellow

Trace the pattern of "Dust of Snow" in the chart below. Follow the example shown for "Paul Revere's Ride." The first one is done for you as an example.

Paul Revere's Ride		Dust of Snow	
hear	*a*	crow	*a*
Revere	*a*		
five	*b*		
alive	*b*		
year	*a*		

ELEVATOR *(pages 162–163)*

Form

Sometimes the first thing you notice about a poem is its **form,** or the way a poem looks on a page. A **line** of poetry may be as short as one word. It may be a phrase or a sentence. Sometimes the lines are placed in groups called **stanzas.** Use the chart below to compare the forms of the two poems "Dust of Snow" and "Elevator."

	Dust of Snow	Elevator
1. Number of lines		
2. Is the poem divided into stanzas? How many?		
3. Does the poem have words that rhyme?		
4. Give an example of rhyming words, if any.		
5. Does the shape of the poem remind you of something? What?		

HAIKU *(pages 164–165)*

Haiku

A **haiku** is a short Japanese poem. It usually has three lines and describes a single moment, feeling, or thing. Read the following haiku and answer the questions below.

> An old quiet pond—
> Frog splashes into water,
> Breaking the silence
>
> —Basho

1. How many syllables are in the first line?

   a. three   b. six   c. five

2. What senses does the image in the first line appeal to?

   a. smelling, hearing   b. seeing, hearing   c. hearing, touching

3. What senses does the image in the second line appeal to?

   a. hearing, seeing   b. smelling, touching   c. seeing, tasting

4. What does the poet mean in the third line by "Breaking the silence"?

   _____

5. What small subject is the speaker describing?

   _____

Make a simple drawing to illustrate the images in this haiku.

Name_____

HAPPY THOUGHT *(pages 166–167)*

Mood

The **mood** of a poem is the way it makes you feel. Writers choose words carefully to create a certain mood. Some poems, like the poem "Happy Thought," make you feel happy. Others can make you feel confused, nervous, or hopeful. Look at the following chart. Think about the words on the left. On the right side, write how these words make you feel.

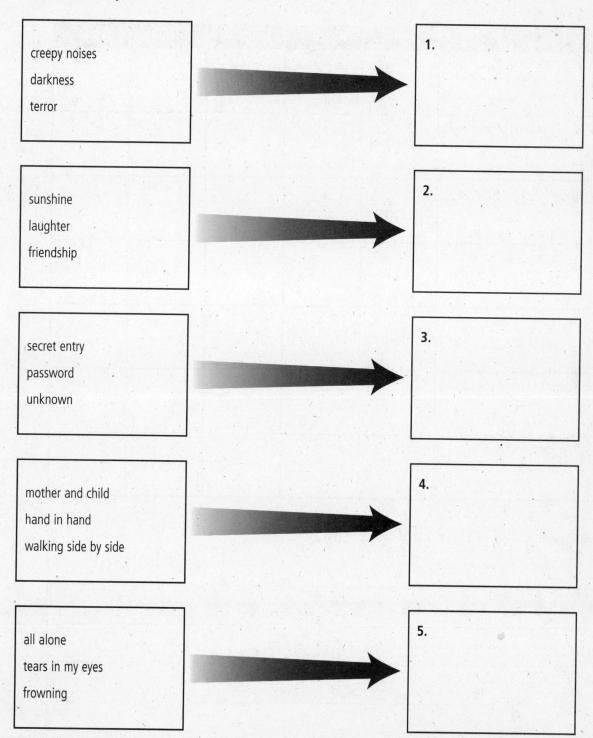

creepy noises
darkness
terror

1.

sunshine
laughter
friendship

2.

secret entry
password
unknown

3.

mother and child
hand in hand
walking side by side

4.

all alone
tears in my eyes
frowning

5.

DAYBREAK IN ALABAMA *(pages 168–169)*

Imagery

Imagery is made up of words and phrases that appeal to the five senses (seeing, hearing, touching, smelling, and tasting). Writers often use imagery to give the reader a feeling for the thing described.

A. For each image, check off the sense or senses it appeals to.

Imagery	Seeing	Hearing	Touching	Smelling	Tasting
1. leaves falling from trees					
2. rain beating on your head					
3. toasted marshmallows					
4. a crowd of crickets chirping					
5. moonlit shadows					
6. scent of orange peels					
7. hushed whispers					

B. Write your own image for each of the five senses.

_____

_____

_____

_____

_____

GRAFFITI *(pages 170–173)*

Speaker

A. The **speaker** in a poem is the voice that talks to the reader. Reread the poem "Graffiti" and answer the following questions.

1. Which of the following details do we know about the speaker?
    a. She is ten years old.
    b. She lives in the city.
    c. It's her birthday.

2. Where does the speaker see the poem?
    a. the train station
    b. on a wall
    c. inside a book

3. What kind of poem does the speaker read?
    a. a long poem
    b. a happy poem
    c. a sad poem

4. What does the word *sweet* mean to the speaker?
    a. a good feeling
    b. a birthday cake
    c. a box of chocolates

    a. unable to make up his or her mind

    b. in trouble

5. How does the speaker feel about graffiti?
    a. happy
    b. upset
    c. afraid

    c. important person

    d. weak spot

B. In your own words, how do you think the speaker feels about her life?

    _____

    _____

UNIT 5 POETRY *(pages 160–173)*

You read the following words in the poems in this unit. They are words you can learn.

> **rued** *v.* felt sorry about
>
> **project** *n.* public housing
>
> **casually** *adv.* in an informal, unplanned way
>
> **slipped** *v.* moved smoothly and easily
>
> **composer** *n.* a creator of music
>
> **graffiti** *n.* drawings or writings on public walls or buildings

A. Write the correct words from the list above in the blanks.

1. A writer of music is a _____.

2. Someone had written _____ on the walls.

3. Many families lived in the apartments of the _____.

4. Business people meet formally, but friends meet _____.

5. His guilty conscience showed that he _____ his poor behavior.

6. Her happiness _____ to joy when she won a million dollars.

B. Use the clues below to figure out which words belong in the boxes.

Down

1. homes for poor people

2. moved easily

3. not formally

4. writing on the wall

Across

5. music writer

6. regretted

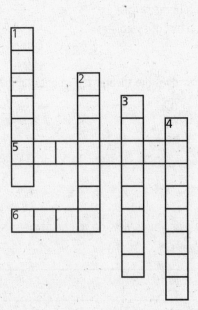

Name_____

HIGH AS HAN HSIN *(pages 176–189)*

Sequence

Writers usually tell about story events in the order they happen. They tell about what happened first, then second, and so on to the story's end. In other words, they tell the story in **sequence.**

Fill in the following boxes with events from "High as Han Hsin."

Event

On the night Han Hsin was born, stars fell and one star _____, and people thought Han Hsin was going to be a _____.

Event

One day, Han Hsin went to neighboring Prince Chin, looking for a _____.

Events

Prince Chin got angry and ordered his soldiers to _____.

Han Hsin escaped the soldiers by acting _____.

Event

Han Hsin joined the army, and because of his great _____ became a general.

Event

Han Hsin beat Prince Chin's first army when he surprised them by having his men climb a mountain using _____ _____ as stairs.

Event

Han Hsin beat Prince Chin's second army when he had his men cross a river on _____ _____.

Event

Han Hsin beat Prince Chin's third army when he scared the soldiers by _____ _____.

Event

Han Hsin won the war and became _____, known as the first man to _____.

HIGH AS HAN HSIN *(pages 176–189)*

Style

Different authors write in different ways. The way they write is called their **style.** Sometimes the writer uses an unusual order in which the verb comes before the subject in sentences.

> Inverted order: Up into the sky <u>went</u> the <u>rocket</u>. (verb: went; subject: rocket)

> Normal order: The <u>rocket</u> <u>went</u> up into the sky. (subject: rocket; verb: went)

A. Rewrite each sentence from "High as Han Hsin" in the usual order. The first one is begun for you.

1. Through the hole in its center grew a bamboo tree.

    A bamboo tree _____

2. Down crashed the heavy weapon.

    _____

3. As he wrote, came hungry ants.

    _____

4. Up went Han and his men.

    _____

5. In strategy lay the only hope.

    _____

B. For each pair, circle the letter of the sentence that is written in inverted order, that is, with the verb coming before the subject.

1. a. Out of the night came the cry of a wolf.
   b. The cry of a wolf came out of the night.

2. a. Upon the island lived many ants.
   b. Many ants lived upon the island.

3. a. Weeping willow trees grew by the stream.
   b. By the stream grew weeping willow trees.

4. a. The tired runners raced across the finish line.
   b. Across the finish line raced the tired runners.

Name_____

Context Clues

Context clues are clues in the text that help readers understand the meanings of words. In a **restatement clue,** writers say the word in a different way. In a **contrast clue,** writers explain a word by giving its opposite. In a **general context clue,** writers give hints about the word's meaning.

Look for context clues. Write the definition of each **boldfaced** word or phrase.

1. One large star **mounted** higher and higher the while its companions fell.

   Mounted means _____.

2. An old astrologer said: "Hush, ***Chieh Kuo*** [Dunce]."

   Chieh Kuo means _____.

3. The old astrologer said, "Hush, ***Sha Tzu*** [Imbecile]."

   Sha Tzu means _____.

4. You—are ***Ko Tsao*** [Little hopping insect].

   Ko Tsao means _____.

5. He was bitter because the troops had mistaken Han's cunning for **imbecility**.

   Imbecility means _____.

6. Near by was a melon patch. The melons were large in their ripeness. Upon a huge striped ***hsi kua*** the boy sat him down and wept.

   Hsi kua is a _____.

7. A fire destroyed the army **muster roll.** Han Hsin quickly wrote a new list.

   A **muster roll** is a _____.

8. How could they know that the flapping was caused by a man-made thing, later to be named "***feng cheng***" [kite]?

   Feng cheng means _____.

HIGH AS HAN HSIN *(pages 176–189)*

Words to Know

imbecile   idiotic   wits   ambush   cunning

A. Circle the letter beside the word or words that mean the same as the **boldfaced** word.

1. Sarah thought that she was smart and therefore not an **imbecile.**

   a. stupid person   b. shy person   c. loud person   d. young person

2. Darren used his **wits** to win the trivia game.

   a. muscles   b. friends   c. quick thinking   d. jokes

3. The celebrity was surprised by an **ambush** of demanding reporters.

   a. meal   b. attack   c. gift   d. hug

4. I felt **idiotic** when I arrived at school and realized that I had forgotten my backpack!

   a. confused   b. stupid   c. sad   d. happy

5. With great **cunning,** the detective tricked the suspect into telling the truth.

   a. skill in fooling   b. skill in fighting   c. skill in shouting   d. skill in running

B. Use the **Words to Know** to fill in the blanks. After you have finished, use the boxed letters to fill in the answer to the bonus question.

If you want to fool somebody, you want to be this.   ☐ __ __ __ __ __ __

This is something that would take you by surprise.   __ __ __ __ __ ☐

You can use these to get yourself out of a sticky situation.   __ ☐ __ __

The town fool could also be called this.   __ __ __ __ __ __ ☐ __

I felt this way after I dropped the meal on the ground.   __ __ ☐ __ __ __ __

What is the Chinese word for "good omen" that the old astrologer talked about? _____

Writing Activity

Write a three- or four-line rap, using at least two of the **Words to Know.**

FOR WANT OF A HORSESHOE NAIL *(pages 190–193)*

Summarizing

Summarizing means retelling the important ideas from a text in a shortened form and in your own words.

Write in the blanks in each box to state the most important ideas and details from "For Want of a Horseshoe Nail." Then complete the summary in the last box. Use as few words as possible to write the summary while still including the important ideas.

Richard the Third's army was about to

_____

_____

_____

_____.

Richard's horse needed

_____.

The blacksmith didn't have

enough _____
so one of the horse's shoes
was not _____

_____.

As Richard rode his horse in

battle, _____

_____, and
Richard was thrown from the horse.

Without Richard to encourage

them, his troops _____

_____ and lost the

_____.

Summary:

When Richard's horse's shoe lost a nail during an important battle,

_____

_____

_____

_____.

FOR WANT OF A HORSESHOE NAIL (pages 190–193)

Historical Fiction

Historical fiction is a blend of fact and fiction. It is set in a real time and place in the past. But the writer imagines many of the thoughts, feelings, and words of the characters. Some parts of historical fiction are factual. Other parts are made up by the writer.

Read each passage below from "For Want of a Horseshoe Nail." Decide if it tells something that can probably be found in records or something that the writer has made up. Put a check in the correct column.

Passage from "For Want of a Horseshoe Nail"	Facts from records	Made up by writer
1. King Richard the Third was preparing for the fight of his life. An army led by Henry, Earl of Richmond, was marching against him. The contest would determine who would rule England.	_____	_____
2. "You'll have to wait," the blacksmith answered. "I've shoed the king's whole army the last few days, and now I've got to get more iron."	_____	_____
3. "I can't wait," the groom shouted impatiently. "The king's enemies are advancing right now, and we must meet them on the field. Make do with what you have."	_____	_____
4. The armies clashed, and Richard was in the thick of the battle. He rode up and down the field, cheering his men and fighting his foes.	_____	_____
5. He was barely halfway across the field when one of the horse's shoes flew off. The horse stumbled and fell, and Richard was thrown to the ground.	_____	_____
6. His army had fallen to pieces, and his troops were busy trying to save themselves. A moment later Henry's soldiers were upon Richard, and the battle was over.	_____	_____

FOR WANT OF A HORSESHOE NAIL *(pages 190–193)*

Multiple-Meaning Words

Multiple-meaning words are words with more than one meaning. Readers must think about how a multiple-meaning word is used in the text to choose the correct meaning.

A. Read each sentence and the definitions for the underlined word. Then write the letter of the correct definition in the blank before the sentence.

_____ **1.** The battle would decide who would be the <u>ruler</u> of England.

a. person in charge   b. strip marked off with units for measuring

_____ **2.** The blacksmith didn't have enough <u>iron</u> for nails.

a. a heavy metal   b. a device that is heated to press cloth

_____ **3.** Richard urged his troops, "<u>Press</u> forward!"

a. to hug closely   b. to attack

_____ **4.** Richard rode toward the broken <u>line</u> and urged the soldiers to turn.

a. words that an actor says   b. soldiers in a row

B. Choose the correct meaning for the underlined word in each sentence below. Then write the correct letter in the blank before the sentence.

_____ **1.** Both players ran in to <u>field</u> the ball.

_____ **2.** We must meet the enemy on the <u>field</u>.

a. to catch or pick up a batted ball   b. place where a battle is fought

_____ **3.** On the knight's armor was a single red <u>rose</u>.

_____ **4.** The frightened horse <u>rose</u> and ran away.

a. got up   b. a showy flower on a prickly bush

_____ **5.** The blacksmith needed another <u>nail</u> to fasten the horseshoe securely.

_____ **6.** "I just broke another <u>nail</u>!" Sharon said angrily, looking at her hand.

a. hard part that covers a finger or toe
b. narrow fastener that is pounded in

_____ **7.** Rita placed the sign <u>over</u> the store entrance.

_____ **8.** A few minutes later, the battle was <u>over</u>.

a. above   b. finished

FOR WANT OF A HORSESHOE NAIL *(pages 190–193)*

Words to Know

retreat   advancing   determine   reins

A. Write the word that is most like the **boldfaced** word below each blank in the following poem.

We are human.
We are brave.

We _____ which adventures
          decide
will be ours.

_____ toward the wide world of the sun
          Traveling
like wild horses,

and one day we will pull on the _____
                              straps

and _____ into wet caves,
          withdraw
holding onto the warmth.

B. Circle the letter next to the word or words that answer each question correctly.

1. What is the opposite of **advancing?**
    a. moving forward   b. turning back   c. following

2. If you put **reins** on an animal, what do you hope to do?
    a. clean it   b. feed it   c. steer it

3. Which of the following might make you **retreat?**
    a. barking dog   b. birthday present   c. kitchen table

4. If you **determine** which book you will read, which do you do?
    a. decide   b. wonder   c. ignore

C. Sometimes you come across words that sound alike but have different spellings and definitions. These are called **homophones.** For example:

> **rein** *n.* leather strap used to control a horse
> **reign** *v.* to hold power over something (like a king over a country)
> **rain** *n.* falling water

Place the correct homophone in the following sentences.

1. Hold on to the horse's _____ so you won't fall off.

2. In my family, my mother _____ over the dinner table.

Comprehension SkillBuilder

SHOT DOWN BEHIND ENEMY LINES *(pages 194–203)*

Visualizing

To **visualize** a scene means to see it in your mind. Drawing a sketch helps you place details correctly in a scene.

Review the final part of "Shot Down Behind Enemy Lines," after the pilot saw the children outside a village. Find answers to the following questions about the scene. Correct the sketch below as needed.

1. Did the pilot find a hiding place at the bottom of a mountain, partway up, or at the top? Draw an **X** in the sketch to show where Locher was.

2. Where was the village—at the top or near the bottom of the mountain? Draw a square in the sketch to stand for the village.

3. The first time helicopters tried to rescue Locher, they were driven off by enemy planes and ground fire. How many helicopters came the second time? If there are too many helicopters in the sketch, cross off the extra ones.

4. How did Locher get to the helicopter? Complete these steps.

   a. First, the helicopter dropped _____

   _____

   b. Second, Locher _____

   _____

   c. Last, the helicopter _____

   _____

SHOT DOWN BEHIND ENEMY LINES *(pages 194–203)*

Descriptive Details

Writers often want to make a person, place, thing, or event seem real to readers. To do that, they include **descriptive details** about how a thing looks, sounds, feels, smells, or tastes.

Fill in the following cluster graph with descriptive details from "Shot Down Behind Enemy Lines." If you want to write more details from the story, add boxes.

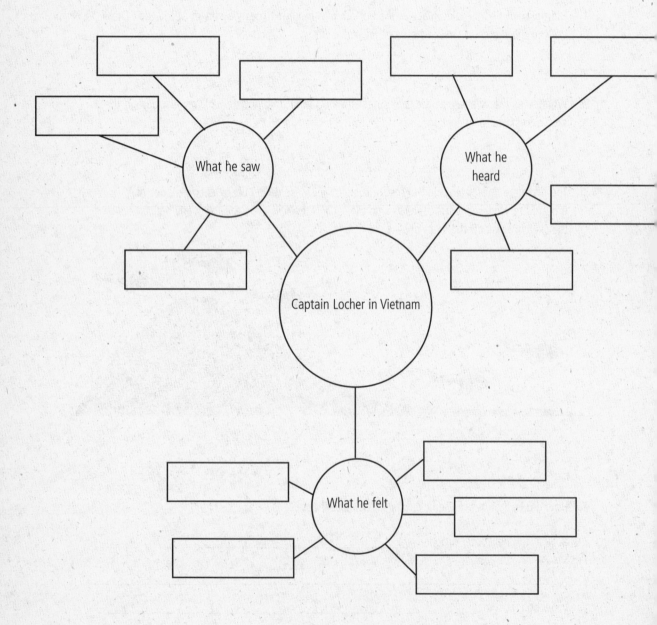

SHOT DOWN BEHIND ENEMY LINES *(pages 194–203)*

Prefixes and Suffixes

A **prefix** is a word part added to the beginning of a base word. The prefix *un-* means "not." A **suffix** is a word part added to the end of a base word. The suffix *-ful* means "full of."

A. Draw a line from each word on the left to its meaning on the right.

1. uninhabited   full of hope

2. hopeful   filled with hate

3. hateful   not harnessed

4. unharnessed   not inhabited

B. Underline a word with a prefix or a suffix in each sentence. Below the sentence, write what the word means.

1. The fall from the jet seemed unreal to Captain Locher.

   _____

2. Locker was careful to cover up his footprints on the ground.

   _____

3. The unripe fruit was all that Locher had to keep from starving.

   _____

4. Locher felt thankful that the pilots had come back for him.

   _____

C. Write the correct word to complete each sentence. One word is not used.

hopeful   unharnessed   hateful

1. _____ from his parachute, Captain Locher hid in the bushes.

2. Locher was _____ that he would be saved.

SHOT DOWN BEHIND ENEMY LINES *(pages 194–203)*

Words to Know

sprawled   navigator   contraption   uninhabited   comrades

A. Write in the blank the word from the list that best completes the sentence.

1. I came home from school to find my cat _____ on the couch.

2. Natasha tried her hardest to open the strange boxlike _____.

3. I drove the car, but my cousin was the _____, reading the map.

4. The army generals were close friends, a group of

_____.

5. The little house in the woods was empty and looked _____.

B. Circle the letter next to the word that doesn't belong. Use the dictionary, if you need to.

1.   a. uninhabited   b. empty   c. crowded

2.   a. machine   b. bread   c. contraption

3.   a. enemies   b. rivals   c. comrades

4.   a. folded   b. spread out   c. sprawled

Writing Activity

Skywriters are pilots. Their job is to write messages in the sky with a trail of smoke from their planes. If you were to send a message to your city by a skywriter, what would it say? Use at least one word from the **Words to Know.**

Name_____

FA MULAN (pages 204–213)

Problem and Solution

Characters in a story usually face one main **problem.** In trying to find a **solution** to that problem, they run into smaller problems. The story tells how the characters solve their problems.

Complete each sentence to tell about Fa Mulan's problems.

What is Fa Mulan's main problem?

She needs to save her _____ and her whole _____.

Why does she face the problem?

The Khan has drafted her _____ to fight the _____.

He is too _____ to go.

Complete the sentences to show how Fa Mulan solves her problems.

Problems	Solutions
1. Fa Mulan wants people to think she is a man.	Fa Mulan _____ _____.
2. Fa Mulan wants to be a good soldier.	She studies _____.
3. It is important that Fa Mulan keep secret the fact that she is a girl.	Fa Mulan always _____.
4. Fa Mulan wants the enemy to think that her troops are disorganized and easy to beat.	She asks her troops to _____ _____ _____.

How does Fa Mulan solve her main problem?

She becomes an excellent _____

who conquers the _____ and then returns to her family.

FA MULAN *(pages 204–213)*

Climax

In a story, tension builds until the climax. The **climax** is the turning point. Tension falls after the climax until the story draws to a close.

A. Read this list of events from "Fa Mulan" carefully. Then look at the plot diagram at the bottom of this page. Write the letter of each event in the correct place on the diagram. There is one blank line for each story event.

a. Fa Mulan discovers that her father has been drafted.

b. Fa Mulan goes to war in his place, keeping secret the fact that she is a girl.

c. Fa Mulan fights bravely in her first battles.

d. Fa Mulan studies how great generals win wars.

e. Fa Mulan fights so bravely and so well that she is made a general.

f. Fa Mulan leads her troops in a clever plan and defeats the enemy.

g. The Khan sends for Mulan. She is afraid that he knows her secret and wants to punish her, but the Khan just wants to thank her. He rewards her by sending her home.

h. At home, Fa Mulan reveals to her fellow soldiers that she is a woman.

i. Fa Mulan's fellow soldiers bow to her.

j. Her father says that she is the greatest woman warrior of all.

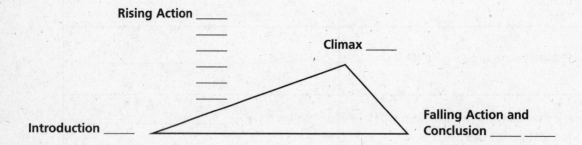

B. Reread the event that you chose as the climax. What was exciting to you about this turning point?

_____

_____

FA MULAN (pages 204–213)

Context Clues

A **synonym** is a word that has the same or almost the same meaning as another word. For example, *brave* and *courageous* are synonyms. When a synonym that you know the meaning of appears in the same sentence or paragraph as a new word, it can help you figure out the new word's meaning.

A. In each sentence there is a **boldfaced** word and a synonym. Find the synonym of the boldfaced word in each sentence. Write it on the line.

1. Fa Mulan's parents saw that she was **anxious** and asked her why she was troubled.

   A synonym of **anxious** is _____.

2. Fa Mulan bravely got up onto her **steed** and rode the horse into battle.

   A synonym of **steed** is _____.

3. Fa Mulan entered the **battle** willingly, but she had never been in combat before.

   A synonym of **battle** is _____.

4. The soldiers wanted to **preserve** their nation and knew that only war could save it.

   A synonym of **preserve** is _____.

5. Fa Mulan's **valor** made her famous, and her courage also brought her the command of a whole army.

   A synonym of **valor** is _____.

B. Circle the word that is a synonym of the **boldfaced** word.

1. **veteran** soldiers   experienced   new

2. **spirited** horse   shy   fiery

3. calm horse's **whicker**   scream   whinny

4. a **ragtag** mob   disorganized   proper

5. **grateful** family   cruel   thankful

FA MULAN *(pages 204–213)*

Words to Know

scrolls   stallion   veterans   fatal   daring

A. In each blank, write the word that best fits the sentence.

1. The sun shone off the strong back of the _____ as he galloped across the beach.

2. Laura was a brave skateboarder; her tricks were very _____.

3. The museum guide would not unroll the _____ because the paper was too old.

4. Todd's grandfathers are _____ because they are no longer in the army.

5. Typhoid fever is a dangerous disease that can be _____.

B. Write **true** or **false** in the blanks.

_____ **1.** People who have just entered the army are called **veterans**.

_____ **2.** **Stallions** can give birth to baby horses.

_____ **3.** If you are trying something new or dangerous, you are **daring.**

_____ **4.** Losing a lot of blood can be **fatal.**

_____ **5.** If you'd like to see **scrolls,** you can go to the video store and rent some.

Writing Activity

Imagine you are a reporter for a newspaper during a war. Using one or two of the **Words to Know,** write a headline for something you might see during a battle.

TWO WERE LEFT *(pages 216–221)*

Predicting

Readers **predict** when they guess what will happen next. Good readers use clues from the story to make their predictions.

Read each story below. Write the clues from the story in the **Detail** boxes of the chart. Some have been done for you. Use the clues to make a prediction. Write it in the **Prediction** box.

1. In "Two Were Left," a pilot happens to see something flashing on the ice. He flies closer and discovers two shapes. The pilot lands his plane and finds the boy and his dog. Noni is unconscious and Nimuk is weak and unable to move.

Detail 1	Detail 2	Detail 3	Detail 4
Pilot sees something flashing on the ice.	He flies closer and sees _____ _____ .	He lands the plane and finds _____ .	Both boy and dog are in bad shape.

Prediction

The pilot will _____
_____ .

2. The dog team runs quickly across the snowy tundra. The snow is falling harder now, but they keep moving. Their strong legs and large, hairy feet keep them from sinking into the deep snowdrifts. Their strong sense of smell tells them home is nearby.

Detail 1	Detail 2	Detail 3	Detail 4
Dog team runs across tundra.	Snow _____ _____ .	The dogs stay on top of _____ _____ .	The dogs smell that _____ _____ .

Prediction

The dogs will _____
_____ .

TWO WERE LEFT *(pages 216–221)*

Suspense

Suspense is the growing feeling of tension and excitement felt by a reader. In "Two Were Left," the writer uses the plot and setting to create suspense. One event builds upon another, leaving the reader guessing at what will happen next. The writer carefully chooses words and details to add more suspense.

A. Number the events from "Two Were Left" in the correct order. Then underline at least one word in each sentence that adds to the suspense. The first item in the list has been marked for you.

_____ "One of us will soon be <u>eating</u> the other, Noni thought. <u>So</u> . . ."

_____ "The dog growled . . . as he . . . circled the boy's body. And Noni was sick with fear."

_____ When Noni finished the knife, he called to Nimuk. Now! Now was the time to strike!

_____ As Noni sharpened the slab of iron, "it seemed . . . that the dog's eyes glowed more brightly as night waned."

_____ "He felt the dog's feet against his leg, the hot rush of Nimuk's breath against his neck."

_____ Noni threw the knife away and with "empty hands outstretched he stumbled toward the dog, and fell."

B. In your own words, tell how the setting of "Two Were Left" adds to the suspense.

_____

_____

_____

_____

_____

Vocabulary SkillBuilder

TWO WERE LEFT *(pages 216–221)*

Structural Analysis

To understand a new word, try to break it into smaller parts that have meaning. Look at prefixes, suffixes, base words, and roots for hints. For example, if you break *inedible* into *in-ed-ible,* the word part *-ed* might remind you of *eat,* and you might guess that *inedible* means "not able to be eaten." If you do not know the meanings of the word parts, or enough of the word parts, use a dictionary.

A. Compare the words in each item. Underline any word part that appears in all three.

1. embellish   emblaze   embitter

2. intractable   traction   tractor

3. labored   laborious   laboratory

4. legal   legitimate   legate

5. incredulous   credit   incredible

6. estimate   inestimable   estimation

B. Which word in Exercise A does each item describe? Write that word on the blank.

_____ **1.** Source: *tractus,* a form of a Latin verb meaning "to draw or pull"
        Meaning: someone or something that pulls

_____ **2.** Source: *estimer,* an Old French verb meaning "to decide the value of"
        Meaning: unable to be measured or valued

_____ **3.** Source: *crēdere,* a Latin verb meaning "to trust or believe"
        Meaning: not believing

_____ **4.** Source: *labōrāre,* a Latin verb meaning "to work"
        Meaning: a place where scientists work

_____ **5.** Source: *lēgis,* a form of a Latin noun meaning "law"
        Meaning: having to do with the law

_____ **6.** Source: *bellus,* a Latin adjective meaning "beautiful"
        Meaning: to make beautiful or more beautiful

TWO WERE LEFT *(pages 216–221)*

Words to Know

essential   fashioned   suspiciously   ominously   descended

A. Circle the letter next to the word or phrase that is most similar to the **boldfaced** word.

1. I have often **fashioned** play figures out of clay.
   a. formed   b. destroyed   c. purchased

2. The teacher looked over the perfect test paper **suspiciously.**
   a. without love   b. without sound   c. without trust

3. As Marcos lowered the rope, the flag **descended** from the top of the flagpole.
   a. dropped   b. moved up   c. danced

4. Godzilla appeared **ominously** out of the sea to walk across the burning city.
   a. pleasantly   b. hungrily   c. threateningly

5. I believe it's **essential** to go to college for a high-paying job.
   a. unwise   b. necessary   c. boring

B. Fill in the blanks with the word from the list that best fits the sentence.

1. The gang gathered in front of the building in a threatening way, or _____.

2. As the countdown began, the New Year's Eve ball _____ toward the neon sign.

3. My dentist says that yearly visits are necessary, as they are _____ for healthy teeth and gums.

4. I watched my grandfather as he carved the wood and _____ a cane.

5. The man, _____ and in a distrustful manner, ran out of the store with his arms full of boxes.

Writing Activity

With a partner, draw a small scene in which someone or something is being brave. Write a caption underneath to describe what's happening. Use at least one of the **Words to Know.**

Name_____

Cause and Effect

The **cause** states why something happens. The **effect** tells what happened.

The effects listed below are from the story "Terrible Things." They are not in the correct order. In the chart below, write each effect in the box next to its correct cause.

Effects

1. They decide the forest is quieter and roomier.
2. Most of the animals are taken away in the nets.
3. No one is left in the forest to help the rabbits.
4. The birds are captured and removed.
5. He will not listen to any warnings.

Cause	Effect
The Terrible Things first come to the forest.	_____
All the remaining animals talk about the first visit of the Terrible Things.	_____
The Terrible Things come back again and again.	_____
Big Rabbit is sure the rabbits are safe in the forest.	_____
The Terrible Things come back for the last group of animals.	_____

TERRIBLE THINGS *(pages 222–230)*

Theme

The **theme** of a work of literature is a lesson about life or human behavior that the writer wants to present to the reader.

In the figure below, events from "Terrible Things" are listed in the outer circle. Fill in the missing words. Then decide what lesson the writer is trying to teach. Write a possible theme in the center of the inner circle.

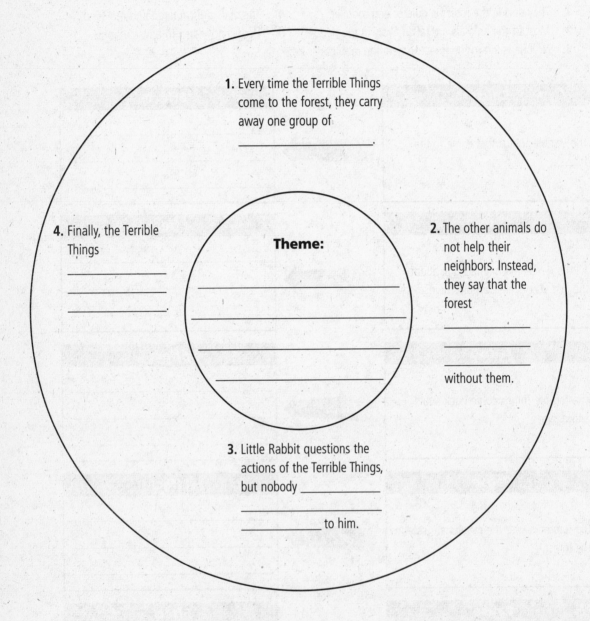

1. Every time the Terrible Things come to the forest, they carry away one group of _____.

2. The other animals do not help their neighbors. Instead, they say that the forest _____ _____ _____ without them.

Theme:
_____
_____
_____
_____

3. Little Rabbit questions the actions of the Terrible Things, but nobody _____ _____ _____ to him.

4. Finally, the Terrible Things _____ _____ _____.

Name_____

TERRIBLE THINGS *(pages 222–230)*

Syllabication

A **syllable** is a word part with one vowel sound. A word is broken into syllables between doubled consonants, as in *mat-ter*. A syllable break usually falls between a base word and a prefix or suffix, as in *re-wind-ing*. Use a dictionary to find syllable breaks in other words.

A. Break these words into syllables. Write the syllables on the lines.

1. clearing _____ _____

2. squirrels _____ _____

3. riddance _____ _____

4. dislike _____ _____

5. prickly _____ _____

B. Choose one syllable from each column to form a word found in the story.

Column 1	Column 2	Column 3	Three-Syllable Word
por	ri	ing	
ner	mer	pine	
shim	cu	ly	
ter	vous	ble	

C. Use the three-syllable words from Exercise B to complete the following sentences.

1. The shiny scales on the fish were _____ in the sunlight.

2. He was shaking with fear as he _____ paced back and forth.

3. People in the village suffered during the _____ storm.

4. The quills of the _____ have barbs, or hooks, at the tip.

TERRIBLE THINGS *(pages 222–230)*

Words to Know

clearing   content   shimmering   quills   bristled

A. On each blank, write the word from the list that best completes the sentence.

1. Sound asleep in her warm bed, Darla was very satisfied, or _____.

2. My favorite part of the evening was watching the lights _____ on the lake.

3. The pioneers prepared a _____ in the forest so they could build their houses.

4. The porcupine's _____ shot up because of the barking dog.

5. I was so scared that even the hairs on the back of my neck _____ with fear.

B. Use the clues below and the **Words to Know** to fill in the puzzle.

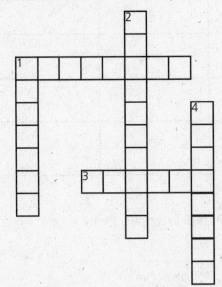

ACROSS

1. land from which trees have been removed
3. sharp, hollow spines

DOWN

1. satisfied
2. flickering
4. stiffened

THE LADY OR THE TIGER? *(pages 232–241)*

Evaluating

Evaluating a piece of writing means judging it according to a set of standards. Every type of literature has standards by which you can judge whether it is good or not.

A. Four types of literature are listed below. Think about what standards you would use to judge each type. Put an **X** before each of those standards.

1. Biography
_____ accuracy of dates
_____ funny dialogue
_____ an exciting conclusion
_____ a description of important events in the subject's life

3. Folk tale
_____ rhythm
_____ interesting characters
_____ a story that is fun to read
_____ the inclusion of a lot of historical details

2. Poem
_____ a story that makes you laugh
_____ rhyme
_____ using language in an interesting way
_____ a surprise ending

4. Drama
_____ silly plot
_____ teaching a lesson
_____ believable characters
_____ realistic dialogue

B. Write two reasons why you think "The Lady or the Tiger?" is a good story or give two reasons why "The Lady or The Tiger?" is not a good story. Be specific; give details from the story that support your opinion.

_____

_____

_____

_____

_____

_____

_____

THE LADY OR THE TIGER? *(pages 232–241)*

Motive

Characters in stories act for specific reasons. These reasons are called **motives.**

Fill in the motives for these characters from "The Lady or the Tiger?" The first one is done for you.

The character's action (or possible)	The character's motive, or reason for the action
1a. The king forced the accused person to choose between two doors; behind one was a _____tiger_____, behind the other, a _____a beautiful lady_____ .	**1b.** The king believed that ____luck____ would decide if the person was _____innocent_____ or _____guilty_____ .
2a. The whole kingdom _____ _____ the trial days. _____ .	**2b.** The people wanted to find out if they would see a _____ or a _____ .
3a. The _____ fell in love with a young man.	**3b.** The young man was very _____ .
4a. When the young man was brought into the arena, he looked at the _____ .	**4b.** He hoped she would let him know _____ _____ _____ .
5a. The princess might point to the door that hid the _____ .	**5b.** She was jealous and did not want the young man to _____ _____ .
6a. The princess might point to the door that hid the _____ .	**6b.** She did not want the young man to _____ .

Context Clues: Definition

To figure out the meaning of a new word, look for clues in the words and phrases around the new word. The passage, or context, may directly state the definition of the word.

A. Use context clues to figure out the meaning of each **boldfaced** word.

1. The king's ancestors had been **barbarians,** that is, wild, uncivilized people.

   Barbarians are _____.

2. People came to see the brave **gladiators,** who were men who fought animals and other men in arenas.

   Gladiators were _____.

3. A **savage**—brutal—tiger hid behind one of the doors.

   Savage means _____.

4. If the person chose the door with the lady, it proved he was **innocent.** In other words, he was not guilty of a crime.

   When you are **innocent,** you are _____.

5. The princess made a **gesture** to the right. A gesture is a movement of the hands.

   A **gesture** is _____.

B. Choose a **boldfaced** word from Exercise A to finish each sentence below.

1. The Roman _____ fought for the entertainment of the people.

2. The man said he did not take part in the robbery and that he was _____.

3. The police officer raised her hands and stopped the traffic with a _____.

4. We watched a video about some _____ animals in Africa.

5. When my brothers forget their table manners, my mother calls them _____.

THE LADY OR THE TIGER? *(pages 232–241)*

Words to Know

barbarians   gladiators   savage   willful   jealousy

A. Fill in the blanks with the word from the list that best completes the sentence.

1. I was surprised by my feelings of _____ when my girlfriend went to the movies with somebody else.

2. My father says that I am a demanding, _____ person who can't take no for an answer.

3. It's amazing that my gentle pet cat is related to the fierce and _____ tiger.

4. Roman _____ fought each other in many games and challenges.

5. In the movie, the brutal _____ killed the beasts in the nastiest battle I've ever seen.

B. Write **true** or **false** in the blanks.

_____ **1.** Gladiators work with plants and flowers.

_____ **2.** If you always follow another person's rules, you are willful.

_____ **3.** Barbarians are wild and sometimes cruel people.

_____ **4.** You may feel some jealousy if your parents give your brother more attention than you.

_____ **5.** Some of the most savage animals are the mouse, turtle, and duck.

Writing Activity

Work with a group and write a two- or three-sentence advertisement. You are trying to convince someone to buy something. It can be anything you choose. Use at least one of the **Words to Know.**

Drawing Conclusions

A **conclusion** is a general statement that you make by combining clues from the story with your own knowledge.

Complete the clues from "Ships That Could Think" and the conclusions that can be drawn from those clues.

Set 1

Clue 1: The captain couldn't steer the *Canton,* so he

_____ .

+

Clue 2: The *Canton* took the crew to _____ who were floating in the water. Then the captain could steer the *Canton* again.

=

Conclusion: _____ somehow knew that the sailors needed help and made sure _____ would save them.

Set 2

Clue 1: The *Frigorifique* seemed to be attacking _____ in revenge.

+

Clue 2: The steersman had lashed the *Frigorifique*'s wheel, so the *Frigorifique* was turning

_____ .

=

Conclusion: The *Frigorifique* was simply _____ , not really

_____ .

SHIPS THAT COULD THINK *(pages 244–251)*

Author's Argument and Evidence

When writers want to persuade readers to agree with them, they present arguments. An **argument** is a series of statements meant to lead readers to a certain conclusion. In their statements, writers give **evidence** that proves their conclusion.

Circle the letter of the statement in each group that does <u>not</u> support the writer's argument.

1. The writer wants readers to come to this conclusion: **This year's weather was bad for farmers.**

   a. Late spring rains flooded the fields and washed out the farmers' seeds.

   b. A lack of rain during June made many crops wither and die.

   c. A hailstorm in August knocked down plants.

   d. Farmers in this area are used to bad weather.

2. The writer wants readers to come to this conclusion: **The buffalo was important in the lives of Native Americans who lived on the Great Plains.**

   a. Plains tribes used buffalo hides to make their homes.

   b. Plains tribes hunted buffalo for their meat.

   c. Plains tribes hunted buffalo on horseback.

   d. Plains tribes used the sharpened bones of buffalo as sewing needles.

3. The writer wants readers to come to this conclusion: **Ships seem to act like humans.**

   a. The *Canton* took her captain and crew to half-starved sailors who needed to be rescued.

   b. The *Canton* was a three-masted whaling ship that was traveling near the island of St. Helena.

   c. The *Canton* would not go in the direction the captain steered her.

   d. Even though the *Frigorifique* was sinking and no one was aboard her, twice she came at the ship that had run into her.

SHIPS THAT COULD THINK *(pages 244–251)*

Specialized Vocabulary

Many fields have their own special words. Context clues can help you understand what these words mean.

In each sentence below, the underlined word has a different meaning than in the companion sentence. Use context clues to choose the meaning that makes the most sense.

1. _____ Ken practiced the <u>hold</u> over and over until he could do it perfectly.

    _____ Water started flooding the <u>hold</u>, and the sailors became frightened.

    a. in wrestling, a way to grab an opponent
    b. the place on a ship where cargo is stored

2. _____ Even with a hole in her <u>hull</u>, the *Frigorifique* stayed afloat.

    _____ Soften the nut's <u>hull</u> by soaking it in water.

    a. outer covering of a fruit or a seed
    b. the frame of a ship or boat

3. _____ The ship started to <u>list</u>, and then it sank.

    _____ The reporter tried to <u>list</u> all the events that would happen at the fair.

    a. to tilt to one side
    b. to mention one after the other

4. _____ They saw smoke pouring from the <u>stack</u> as the ship came at them.

    _____ The programmer looked in the <u>stack</u>, but the information was lost.

    a. the pipe of an engine that lets fumes escape
    b. in computers, a place for storing information for a short time

5. _____ The captain will <u>steer</u> the ship into the island's harbor.

    _____ The cowboy brought down the huge <u>steer</u> with one throw of the rope.

    a. a young ox
    b. to set and hold to a course, as when guiding a ship or a car

SHIPS THAT COULD THINK *(pages 244–251)*

Words to Know

vessel   course   horizon   drifted   emerged

A. Fill in each blank with the correct word from the **Words to Know.**

   1. The beautiful _____ sailed off into shimmering waters.

   2. The fallen tree branch _____ to the river's shore.

   3. Sam and I sat on the hill, watching the sun melt into the _____.

   4. The car sped down the _____.

   5. My sister _____ from her room, dressed in her prom dress.

B. Write **true** or **false** in the blanks before each statement.

   _____ **1.** A **course** is a route.

   _____ **2.** The **horizon** is the part of the eye next to the retina.

   _____ **3.** If you've come into view, you've **emerged.**

   _____ **4.** If your raft has **drifted** upstream, it has stayed where you left it.

   _____ **5.** A **vessel** is something you use to keep your clothing in.

Writing Activity

Use your dictionary to find three meanings for *vessel* and three meanings for *course*. Write three sentences, each using *vessel* with a different meaning. Then write three sentences, each using *course* with a different meaning.

EARTHQUAKES *(pages 252–259)*

Main Idea and Supporting Details

A **main idea** is the most important idea in a paragraph. **Supporting details,** which are found in the rest of the paragraph, tell more about the main idea. Often the main idea is stated in a topic sentence. At other times, the reader must put together details to figure out what the main idea is.

For each exercise below, read the paragraph and then complete the main-idea chart. Complete the main idea in the top box. Fill in the lower boxes with details.

1. Parts of the Earth are always moving. Whole mountains move. Big sections of a continent like North America can move. Even whole continents move. Right now North America and Europe are moving apart.

Main idea: Parts of the Earth are _____ .		

Detail 1: Whole _____ move.	**Detail 2:** Big sections of _____ move.	**Detail 3:** Whole _____ move.

2. During a big earthquake, many buildings fall down. There are also fires. Pipes that carry gas to homes are broken. A spark may set the gas afire. Sometimes firefighters can't fight the flames because water pipes have broken. During an earthquake, dams may break too. Rivers may be blocked by landslides. So there is often flooding in the area of an earthquake.

Main idea: What can happen during a big _____		

Detail 1: Buildings fall down.	**Detail 2:** Fires are started.	**Detail 3:** Floods happen.
Details about buildings: No more details	Details about fires: Sparks set gas from broken _____ on fire. Firefighters can't put out fires because _____	Details about floods: _____ break. _____ block rivers.

EARTHQUAKES *(pages 252–259)*

Text Structure

Writers gather a lot of information. Then they organize it with care so readers will understand and remember it.

Look back at page 255 and at the top of page 256. Then study the chart below. It shows how the writer of "Earthquakes" has organized information about the causes of earthquakes. Complete the chart with examples and details from the science article.

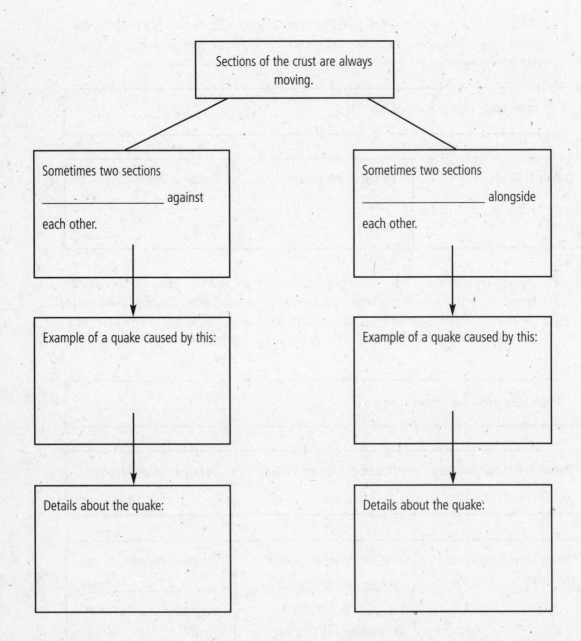

EARTHQUAKES *(pages 252–259)*

Context Clues

Context clues are clues that surround an unfamiliar word or phrase. Look for context clues to the meaning of a new word by looking at the words and phrases around the word.

A. Use context clues to figure out the meaning of each **boldfaced** word from "Earthquakes." Then write the meaning on the line.

1. We live on the outer part of Earth. It is called Earth's **crust.**

Earth's **crust** is _____.

2. Every earthquake has a center. That's where it all begins. Parts of the Earth move up and down or go sideways, and make waves that spread out and go through the whole Earth. They are called **seismic waves.** The word comes from *seismos,* a Greek word meaning to shake. Scientists all over the world measure the waves on **seismometers.**

Seismic waves are _____.

A **seismometer** is _____.

3. Large sections of the Earth's crust are always moving. Sometimes two sections push against each other. The place where they meet is called a **fault.**

A **fault** is _____.

4. The water piled high, making a huge wave that traveled toward the shore. The wave was a wall of water called a **tsunami,** a Japanese word.

A **tsunami** is _____.

B. Use a **boldfaced** word from Exercise A to complete each sentence below.

1. The people ran to high ground to get away from the _____.

2. The scientist checked the _____ to see how strong the

quake was.

3. I would be afraid of earthquakes if I lived near a _____.

EARTHQUAKES *(pages 252–259)*

Words to Know

continent   buckles   topple   erupt   satellites

A. In each blank, write the word from the list that best completes the sentence.

1. My parents were born somewhere within the African _____.

2. My little cousin loves to _____ the blocks after her mother sets them up.

3. Many countries send _____ to orbit the earth to watch the weather.

4. The shelf _____ because there is too much weight on it.

5. I have only seen volcanoes _____ in photographs.

B. Fill in each blank with a word from the list at the top of the page.

1. If you knock something over, you _____.

2. A person faints from the heat and falls, or _____.

3. Asia's land mass makes it the largest _____.

4. If you shake a bottle of soda and then open it, it might

   _____.

5. We get cable television and keep an eye on our weather through _____.

Writing Activity

Have you ever experienced an earthquake or another force of nature such as a tornado or a hurricane? If so, what was it like? If not, what do you imagine it would be like? Write three sentences using at least three of the **Words to Know.**

SPARKY *(pages 260–263)*

Evaluating

Evaluating a piece of writing means judging it. Look at each feature of the piece separately to give a fair evaluation. Back up your opinions with proof from the text.

Evaluate the essay "Sparky" by answering the following questions:

1. How well did the writer describe Sparky in this essay? List at least three things you learned about Sparky.

_____

_____

_____

_____

2. How did the writer show that Sparky was not really a loser? What details made you admire Sparky?

_____

_____

_____

_____

3. How well did the writer explain what made Sparky successful? Which details helped you understand how Sparky succeeded?

_____

_____

_____

_____

4. What is one theme of this essay? Tell why you agree or disagree with the author's message about life.

_____

_____

_____

_____

SPARKY *(pages 260–263)*

Essay

An **essay** is a short work in which the writer explains his or her opinion. The writer may also share a message about life. In "Sparky," the writer shares his thoughts about a loser who became a winner.

Fill in the missing details from the essay "Sparky." Then write the message that you think the author is sharing.

Sparky was a loser at school because he _____

_____

_____

Sparky was a loser at sports because he

_____

_____

_____

Writer's message _____

_____

_____

_____

_____

Sparky became a success when he

_____

_____

_____

Sparky was a loser in relationships because he _____

_____

_____

Sparky never lost faith in his ability to

_____

_____

_____

SPARKY *(pages 260–263)*

Using the Dictionary

A **dictionary** is a book that presents information about words. It lists words in alphabetical order. It gives their pronunciations, parts of speech, and meanings. If more than one meaning is listed for a word, readers must consider the word's context and decide which meaning the writer meant.

A. In each of the following sentences, one word has been underlined. Read the dictionary entry for that word in the box below. Decide which meaning the writer meant. Write the part of speech and the number of the correct meaning on the lines.

	Part of Speech	Number of Definition
1. Otherwise he would <u>content</u> himself with what appeared to be his inevitable mediocrity.	_____	_____
2. Sparky was a loser. He, his classmates . . . everyone knew it. So he <u>rolled</u> with it.	_____	_____
3. He was told to send some samples of his artwork, and the <u>subject</u> for a cartoon was suggested.	_____	_____

---

content (kən tĕnt') *adj*. 1. happy with one's life. *v*. 2. to be satisfied with limitations.

roll (rōl) *n*. 1. a list of names. 2. a small piece of baked dough. *v*. 3. to move or act in a way that lessens damage or pain, as in *roll with the punches*.

subject (sŭb' jĕkt) *adj*. 1. likely to have, as in *subject to fits of sneezing*. *n*. 2. a topic being discussed or considered.

subject (səb jĕkt') *v*. 3. to make to undergo, as in *subjected to ridicule*.

B. Put each list of words in alphabetical order. For each list, write **1** beside the word that would come first in the dictionary, **2** beside the word that would come next, and so on.

_____ match	_____ school	_____ letter
_____ matter	_____ sample	_____ ladder
_____ mutt	_____ subject	_____ latch
_____ melt	_____ stamp	_____ limit
_____ mattress	_____ surf	_____ lather

SPARKY *(pages 260–263)*

Words to Know

submitted   rejection

A. In each blank, write the word from the list that best completes the sentence.

1. I _____ my homework to my teacher at the end of class.

2. My family says that I have to learn how to handle _____.

B. **Prefixes** The prefix **sub-** means "below" or "almost." The prefix **re-** means "again" or "backward." The following words have a **sub-** or **re-** prefix. Read the definitions, then complete each sentence by writing the correct word on the line.

submarine   *n.* a boat that goes underwater

subside   *v.* to sink to a lower or normal level

repulsed   *adj.* driven back or pushed away

reproduce   *v.* to make a copy of

1. Her screams and tears began to _____, and

   she felt much more like herself.

2. I was _____ by all of the smoke in the

   hallway and didn't enter the room.

3. The spies used a _____ to move into enemy

   waters.

4. Luz wanted to _____ the magazine article, so

   she used a photocopy machine.

Writing Activity
Draw your own cartoon. Write a caption using one of the **Words to Know.**

THE ROSWELL INCIDENT *(pages 264–267)*

Fact and Opinion

A **fact** is a statement that can be proved. An **opinion** tells a personal belief, feeling, or idea and cannot be proved.

A. Read each statement and decide whether it is a fact or an opinion. Write **fact** or **opinion** on the line.

1. In July 1947, William Brazel phoned the air force base at Roswell to report that he had found a metal fragment on his ranch. _____

2. Air force officials should show their secret documents to Americans. _____

3. It is scary to think that aliens are visiting Earth. _____

4. We may never learn what really happened at Roswell in 1947. _____

5. Someday the air force will be forced to reveal everything it has learned about flying saucers. _____

6. Americans ought to believe whatever their government tells them. _____

7. Authorities said that the crashed object at Roswell was a weather balloon. _____

8. It is wrong for officials to try to cover up the truth. _____

B. For each box in the chart below, select the correct statements from the list above. Write their numbers on the lines.

Facts	Opinions		
	I know these items are opinions because		
I know these items are facts because there are proofs in public records: _____ and _____	(a) the sentence uses a word like *good* or *bad*: _____ and _____	(b) the sentence uses a word like *may* or *will*: _____ and _____	(c) the sentence uses a word like *should* or *must*: _____ and _____

C. In your opinion, does "The Roswell Incident" present enough facts about what happened in 1947? Explain.

_____

_____

_____

THE ROSWELL INCIDENT *(pages 264–267)*

Author's Perspective

The **author's perspective** is the way he or she feels about a question or topic. Writing that gives only one side of a question is described as **biased.** Writing that presents both sides is described as **balanced.**

A. Read each paragraph. Decide whether it is biased or balanced. Circle your choice.

1. The silly people who believe in flying saucers just will not give up, it seems. Even though patient air force officials have told them over and over again that there are no UFOs, they keep making trouble. When will these pitiful losers get a life?

        biased   balanced

2. Many believers in UFOs say that the air force is covering up the truth about what happened at Roswell. Air force officials insist that they have shared all they know about reports of flying saucers. The debate will likely go on for years.

        biased   balanced

3. Starting in 1947 with the famous Roswell discovery of an alien spaceship, the air force has shown a terrible lack of respect for the people of the United States. Of course, any thinking person knows that officials are covering up important secrets about visits from other planets. What are they trying to hide?

        biased   balanced

B. Read this paragraph and answer the question below.

Foolish scientists are sending out radio messages into space, hoping that someday a creature in outer space will hear them and answer back. This waste of time and money has been going on for far too long. I say forget about imaginary space creatures and concentrate on problems in the real world.

What is the author's perspective about sending radio messages into space?

_____

_____

_____

Name_____

THE ROSWELL INCIDENT *(pages 264–267)*

Word Origins: Greek Roots

The English language contains many words with Greek roots. If you know the meaning of the Greek root, you can more easily guess the meanings of English words that include that root.

Read these Greek roots and their meanings. Then answer the riddles, choosing your answers from the box below.

aut means "self"   *opt* or *ops* means "eye" or "sight"

bi means "life"   *graph* means "writing"

ge means "earth"   *log* means "study of"

biology	autograph	autobiography	geothermal
autopsy	optician	biosphere	graphology
biography	automobile	geology	calligraphy

1. A vehicle that moves by itself is called an _____.

2. The part of earth's crust, water, and air that supports life is the _____.

3. If *therm* means "temperature," then the word _____ describes heat in the earth.

4. The story of a person's life, when written by someone else, is a _____.

5. If *call* means "beautiful," then _____ means "beautiful writing."

6. In an _____, a doctor himself or herself looks carefully at a dead body.

7. The study of the earth is called _____.

8. Someone who makes eyeglasses is called an _____.

9. The story of a person's life, when written by himself or herself, is an

    _____.

10. When you sign your _____, you write your own name.

11. The study of life is called _____.

12. The study of writing is called _____.

Name_____

THE ROSWELL INCIDENT *(pages 264–267)*

Words to Know

authorities   spindly   bizarre   procedure   rumor

A. In each blank, write the word from the list that best completes the sentence.

1. Although Laura was thin and _____, she had a great deal of strength.

2. The kind doctor explained the _____ he would perform.

3. The parrot was weird; it was a _____ bird.

4. I didn't pay any attention to the _____ that our school was shutting down.

5. Some situations call for the _____ to be present and make decisions.

B. For each sentence, circle the word or phrase that is most similar in meaning to the **boldfaced** word.

1. My grandmother called the **authorities** when she saw someone outside of her window.

   a. dogs   b. people in power   c. photographers

2. The **spindly** man wore a coat three sizes too big.

   a. thin   b. big   c. rude

3. Our counselor taught us the proper **procedure** for performing the Heimlich maneuver.

   a. book   b. tool   c. way

4. There was a **rumor** that the famous actress would visit the town.

   a. unproven information   b. fact   c. history

5. Some of the most **bizarre** creatures can be found at the zoo.

   a. strange   b. average   c. expensive

Writing Activity

Tabloid newspapers report news that doesn't seem very believable. Pretend you are writing for the tabloid press. Make up a story about something as wild as you can imagine. With a partner, write a headline and the first paragraph of your story. Use at least two of the **Words to Know.**

THE JADE STONE *(pages 270–280)*

Predicting

When readers guess what will happen next in a story, they are making **predictions.** Thinking about clues in the story can help readers make good predictions.

A. The emperor in "The Jade Stone" says he will punish Chan Lo for carving fish instead of a dragon. Put an **X** before the clues that would lead readers to predict that the emperor will *not* actually punish him.

_____ **1.** The emperor keeps dreaming about fish.

_____ **2.** The emperor is very angry that Chan Lo had not carved a dragon.

_____ **3.** The emperor orders Chan Lo thrown in prison.

_____ **4.** When the emperor's advisers ask him what punishment he has chosen, he stalls and tells them his dreams have not yet decided.

_____ **5.** The emperor sits near the pool, gazing at the jade stone for hours.

_____ **6.** The emperor calls Chan Lo a brave man.

B. Read this story and think about what might come next. Then answer the questions below.

Tommy waited eagerly at the check-out counter. He counted all the money in his pocket and made sure he had enough for his mother's birthday gift. For months he had been saving nickels, dimes, and quarters. When he exchanged his coins for dollar bills at the bank, he walked out with $18.22. It wasn't enough to buy his mother the lovely silk scarf that caught her attention at the store. However, it was certainly enough for a set of perfumed candles and a card, he thought. Tommy calculated the total would be $17.01 before taxes. Finally, it was his turn in line. As he handed the cashier the items, he hoped he had enough money to pay for them.

1. What do you predict will happen next? Circle the letter of your choice.

a. Tommy will have enough money to buy his mother candles and a card.

b. Tommy will not have enough money to pay for the gift.

2. Tell why you think this will happen. Give at least one clue in the story that led you to your prediction.

_____

_____

THE JADE STONE *(pages 270–280)*

Conflict

A **conflict** is a problem or struggle. An **external conflict** takes place between two characters or between characters and a force of nature. An **internal conflict** takes place within a character.

There are three conflicts in "The Jade Stone." The following statements describe both sides of each of the three conflicts. Write each statement in the correct chart below.

Chan Lo wants to listen to the stone.

Chan Lo wants to carve three fish.

Chan Lo wants to please the emperor.

The emperor wants to punish Chan Lo.

The emperor wants Chan Lo to carve a dragon.

The emperor is not sure he should punish Chan Lo.

Internal Conflict

One side of the conflict	The other side

External Conflict

One side of the conflict	The other side

Internal Conflict

One side of the conflict	The other side

THE JADE STONE *(pages 270–280)*

Latin Roots

Many words in the English language come from words in the Latin language. Knowing the meaning of **Latin roots** will help you understand many English words.

A. Match the words in this list with the Latin words below. Look for similarities in spelling and meaning.

punish	advice	apprentice	emperor	reflection	terrible
adviser	terrify	reflex	punishment	imperial	apprehend

1. *terrēre,* "to frighten"　_____　_____

2. *pūnīre,* "to punish"　_____　_____

3. *ad-,* "to" + *vidēre,* "to see"　_____　_____

4. *imperātor,* "commander"　_____　_____

5. *reflectere,* "to bend back"　_____　_____

6. *apprehendere,* "to seize"　_____　_____

B. Use seven of the words in Exercise A to complete these sentences. Thinking of the meaning of their Latin roots will help you. One answer should show the plural form of the word.

1. The _____ was the commander of all China.

2. The emperor looked to his _____ for help.

3. A young man became an _____ to Chan Lo so that he could learn all about carving stones.

4. The emperor looked at the _____ of the jade fish in the water.

5. Chan Lo expected a horrible _____ for not carving what the emperor wanted.

6. Chan Lo was afraid of the _____ punishment he thought he was going to receive.

7. Although Chan Lo disobeyed him, the emperor decided not to _____ him but to reward him instead.

THE JADE STONE *(pages 270–280)*

Words to Know

apprentice   entangled   defy

A. Fill in the blanks with a word from the list above that best completes the sentence.

1. I couldn't say a word—it was as if my tongue had become _____.

2. I wanted to learn the work, so I became an _____ in the shop.

3. It's not a good idea to _____ my father's orders.

B. Match the word with its correct definition.

_____ **1.** apprentice   a. resist with boldness

_____ **2.** entangled   b. one who is learning a job

_____ **3.** defy   c. twisted together

C. Circle the word or phrase that is most similar to the **boldfaced** word.

1. The cranky old man yelled at the **apprentice** after he dropped the instrument.

   a. veteran   b. boss   c. beginner

2. Soon I found myself **entangled** in the wires, unable to move.

   a. twisted   b. loose   c. asleep

3. I **defy** the advice of my friends and do just what I want to.

   a. obey   b. resist   c. respect

Writing Activity

Write a couple of sentences about something you've done that you're especially proud of. Use at least one of the **Words to Know.**

Name_____

THE STOLEN PARTY *(pages 282–293)*

Making Judgments

When you **judge** an element of a story, such as a character or the character's actions, you decide whether you approve or disapprove. To make a fair judgment, you must not only think of how you feel. You must also find details in the story that support your judgment.

Read each statement below from "The Stolen Party" and circle **agree** or **disagree.** Then tell why you feel this way. Use a detail from the story to support your judgment.

1. Rosaura's mother is an open-minded person.   **agree**   **disagree**

    I feel this way because

    _____

    _____

    _____

2. Rosaura is too pleased with herself during the party.   **agree**   **disagree**

    I feel this way because

    _____

    _____

    _____

3. It is wrong for Señora Ines to offer money to Rosaura   **agree**   **disagree**
    at the end of the party.

    I feel this way because

    _____

    _____

    _____

4. The title of this story doesn't fit the story.   **agree**   **disagree**

    I feel this way because

    _____

    _____

    _____

THE STOLEN PARTY *(pages 282–293)*

Theme

The **theme** of a story is a lesson about life or human behavior that the author shares with the reader.

In "The Stolen Party" the **dialogue,** or words spoken by the characters, helps the reader to understand the theme. Read the dialogue in the outer circle of the figure below. Then, in the inner circle, write a possible theme of the story.

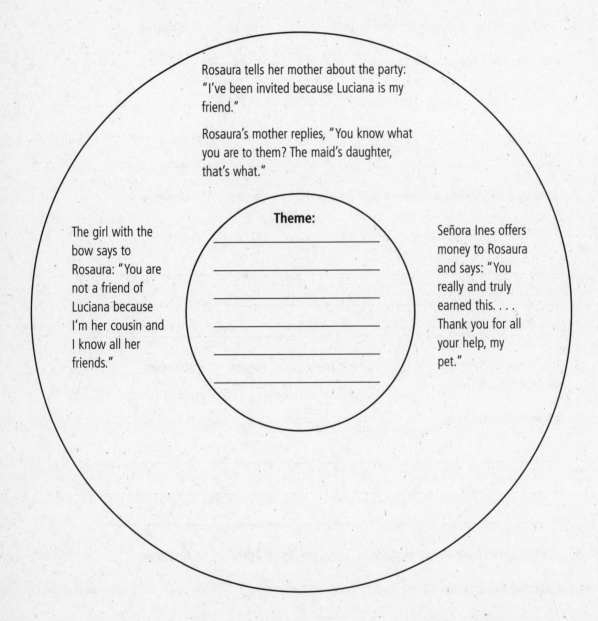

Rosaura tells her mother about the party: "I've been invited because Luciana is my friend."

Rosaura's mother replies, "You know what you are to them? The maid's daughter, that's what."

The girl with the bow says to Rosaura: "You are not a friend of Luciana because I'm her cousin and I know all her friends."

Theme:
_____
_____
_____
_____
_____
_____

Señora Ines offers money to Rosaura and says: "You really and truly earned this. . . . Thank you for all your help, my pet."

Name_____

THE STOLEN PARTY *(pages 282–293)*

Multiple-Meaning Words

When a word has more than one meaning, it has **multiple meanings.** Choose the correct definition by thinking about how the word is used in context.

A. Read each sentence and the definitions for the underlined word. Write the letter of the correct meaning on the blank.

_____ **1.** Rosaura could not help but <u>fix</u> her eyes on the monkey.

    a. to repair or mend   b. to stare at an object steadily

_____ **2.** Serving the cake gave her a sense of <u>power</u> over the other children.

    a. energy or force that can do work   b. control or authority

_____ **3.** The birthday cake rested on a <u>delicate</u> flowered plate.

    a. easily broken; fragile   b. mild tasting or lightly flavored

_____ **4.** Hearing Rosaura being called well-behaved made her mother <u>beam</u> with delight.

    a. a large piece of wood used in building   b. smile brightly

B. Read each sentence below. Then write the letter of the correct definition of the underlined word on the blank.

_____ **1.** This ticket will <u>admit</u> you to the concert.

_____ **2.** She refused to <u>admit</u> she made a mistake.

    a. accept as true

    b. allow to enter

_____ **3.** Maria's sister works at a machine <u>shop</u>.

_____ **4.** We will <u>shop</u> for the new computer tomorrow.

    a. a place where a special kind of work is done

    b. to visit stores in order to buy things

_____ **5.** Juan used a <u>balance</u> to measure the chemicals.

_____ **6.** After six months, you must pay off the <u>balance</u> of the loan.

    a. an instrument for weighing

    b. the amount still owed after partial payment

THE STOLEN PARTY (pages 282–293)

Words to Know

approve   employee   compliment   offended   boisterous

A. Fill in the blanks with the word from the list that best completes the sentence.

1. Natalie received a _____ from the teacher on her research paper.

2. I was hired as an _____ of the local grocery store.

3. Jackson was _____ by the hurtful remarks made by his friends.

4. My grandmother did not _____ of my new hair color.

5. Nikki tried to calm the _____ kids she babysat by giving them ice cream.

B. **Analogies** An analogy shows a relationship between words:

poodle : dog :: goldfish : fish

A poodle **is to** a dog **as a** goldfish **is to** a fish.

A poodle is a type of dog; a goldfish is a type of fish.

To complete an analogy, look at the first pair of words and decide how they are related. Then find a word that relates to the word in the second part in the same way.

Use a word from the **Words to Know** list above to fill in the analogies below.

1. chef : restaurant :: _____ : company

2. quiet: silent :: noisy: _____

3. understand: misunderstand :: _____ : disapprove

C. **Homophones** are words that sound alike but have different spellings and definitions. For example:

compliment (noun) words of praise, admiration, or congratulations

complement (noun) something that completes or fills; makes a whole

Fill in the blanks with the correct homophone.

1. A soda or drink will _____ a large, thin-crust pizza.

2. The doctor gave me a _____ on my recovery.

Name_____

ACCEPTANCE *(pages 294–303)*

Cause and Effect

Events often are related by cause and effect. The first event **causes** something to happen. The second event, the **effect,** tells what happened as a result of the first one.

Fill in the boxes to show causes and effects in "Acceptance."

Cause	Effect
For the first time, Jane followed a group of chimpanzees in the thick forest.	The chimps _____ _____ _____.
One time Jane lay down on the ground in order not to scare some chimps.	Not recognizing her, one large male chimp _____ _____ _____.
Dazed by the blow, Jane _____ _____ _____.	The angry chimp ran away quickly.
_____ _____ _____	David Graybeard gently grasped Jane's hand.
Jane realized the need to help chimps everywhere.	_____ _____ _____
_____ _____	Some medical researchers now follow her suggestions.

ACCEPTANCE *(pages 294–303)*

Author's Purpose

The special reason why an author writes is called the **author's purpose.**

Read each paragraph below. The author may have had more than one purpose for writing it. Circle the possible purpose (or purposes) for each of the paragraphs.

1.   Soon after Jane Goodall arrived in Gombe, she had a frightening experience with the chimpanzees in the deep forest. Later she wrote, "My knees were shaking when I got up. But there was the sense of excitement that comes when danger has come and left one unharmed. And the chimpanzees were surely less afraid of me now."

   inform   entertain   express feelings   persuade

2.   When speaking to audiences, Jane often ends by saying, "If a chimpanzee . . . can reach out across the species barrier to help a human friend in need, then surely we, with our deeper capacity for compassion and understanding, can reach out to help the chimpanzees who need us, so desperately, today."

   inform   entertain   express feelings   persuade

3.   Jane Goodall has told medical researchers who use chimps in their work, "The suffering of chimps can be reduced by putting them in bigger cages, exposing them to the outdoors, and allowing them more contact with each other."

   inform   entertain   express feelings   persuade

4.   Many researchers have tried to "talk" with chimpanzees by teaching them to use symbols. Two such "pupils" were Sherman and Austin. When the chimpanzees proved they knew the meaning of many symbols, a researcher remarked, "Those chimps are champs!"

   inform   entertain   express feelings   persuade

5.   The four types of apes are chimpanzees, gibbons, gorillas, and orangutans. Chimps are considered the most intelligent of the apes. They are curious and playful and can be easily trained in many tasks.

   inform   entertain   express feelings   persuade

ACCEPTANCE *(pages 294–303)*

Context Clues

To find out the meaning of a new word, look for clues in words and phrases within the sentence. These hints in the passage are called **context clues.**

A. Use context clues to determine the meaning of the boldfaced word.

1. Jane moved **cautiously** among the chimpanzees, taking care to be safe in the thick forest.

   Cautiously means _____.

2. It was difficult to see the chimps through the thick **vegetation.** The closely growing plants hid them from Jane's view.

   Vegetation means _____.

3. At first, some of the larger chimps were quick to attack. Later they became less **aggressive.**

   Aggressive means _____.

4. The chimpanzee population has **dwindled** over the years. There are fewer chimps today than when Jane Goodall began studying them.

   Dwindle means _____.

5. Medical researchers try to find another way, or **alternative,** to using chimps in their research.

   Alternative means _____.

B. Use the boldfaced words in Exercise A to complete each sentence.

1. The supply of pizza quickly _____ as the hungry students entered the cafeteria.

2. Chad moved _____ over the rocky ground until he safely reached the other side.

3. One very _____ guard dog went after the intruder.

4. The only _____ to walking down the long trail is riding a mule.

5. Deep in the rain forest, the explorers used long, heavy knives to clear a path through the _____.

ACCEPTANCE *(pages 294–303)*

Words to Know

glaring   aggressive   compassion   brutal   instinctively

A. On each blank, write the word from the list that best fits the sentence.

1. Flying south is what birds do naturally, or _____.

2. My grandmother worked at an animal shelter because she had such _____ for animals.

3. Mr. Chen thought boxing was far too violent, cruel, and _____.

4. My sister's _____ eyes showed that she was angry.

5. The kids who forced their way to the front of the line were very _____.

B. On the blank, write the letter of the correct definition. Use the dictionary if you need to.

_____ **1.** compassion   a. extremely rough

_____ **2.** glaring   b. forceful

_____ **3.** aggressive   c. staring in anger

_____ **4.** instinctively   d. by natural action; without thinking

_____ **5.** brutal   e. concern for the suffering of others

Writing Activity

Suppose you are an animal expert. Write three sentences about one animal. Use at least one of the **Words to Know.**

GROWING UP IN A WORLD OF DARKNESS *(pages 304–317)*

Main Idea

The **main idea** is the most important thought in a paragraph. The main idea may be stated directly in a topic sentence. The topic sentence may appear anywhere in the paragraph. Other times, readers must figure out the main idea that brings together all the thoughts in the paragraph.

A. Find the stated main idea in each of these paragraphs from "Growing Up in a World of Darkness." Underline the topic sentence.

1. Stevie was a lucky child in many ways. He was lucky to have two brothers close enough to him in age not to understand at first about his blindness and to expect him to do many of the things they did. He was also lucky to have a mother and a father . . . who understood how important sound was to him, and how important it was for him to learn to identify things he could not see by their sound.

2. "I don't really feel my hearing is any better than yours," Stevie says now; "we all have the same abilities, you know." . . . Encouraged by his family, Stevie used his hearing more and more as he grew older. He learned how to tell birds apart by their calls, and to tell trees apart by the sound their leaves made as they rustled in the wind. He learned to tell when people were tired or annoyed or pleased by listening to the tone of their voices.

B. Circle the letter of the sentence that states the main idea of each paragraph.

1. By the age of two, Stevie used spoons to make rhythmic sounds. Later, he beat on cardboard drums and used a small harmonica. He learned to play the piano and bongo drums. He also experimented with his voice.

   a. Stevie found many ways to make sounds and music.

   b. Stevie often listened to the radio.

2. First, Ronnie White took him around the studio, allowing Stevie to touch all the instruments and recording equipment. Then Stevie met Berry Gordy, the president of the company. Stevie sang and played the drums and harmonica for him. Berry Gordy immediately signed Stevie to a long contract.

   a. Stevie worked for Hitsville USA for ten years.

   b. Stevie's audition at the Hitsville USA recording studio was exciting.

GROWING UP IN A WORLD OF DARKNESS *(pages 304–317)*

Problem and Solution

In most stories, characters meet problems in their lives. They must find ways to solve the problems they face. The events in a story or article may be organized to describe a **problem** and then show its **solution.**

The biography "Growing Up in a World of Darkness" describes several problems that Stevie Wonder had to solve. In the chart below, either the problem or a solution is listed. Fill in the missing problems and solutions.

Problem	Solution
1. _____ _____ _____	1. As a child, Stevie developed his sense of hearing so he could identify things by the way they sounded.
2. Sometimes at night, Stevie did not feel part of the world when everything around him was silent.	2. _____ _____ _____
3. _____ _____ _____	3. Stevie told his mother that he was happy being blind. He said it was a gift from God.
4. In order to live as normal a life as possible, Stevie needed to learn many things not taught to children with sight.	4. _____ _____ _____
5. _____ _____ _____	5. Stevie received a drum set from the Lions Club. Friendly neighbors gave him a real harmonica and piano.
6. On the school bus, Stevie felt a little ashamed because he listened to a black radio station.	6. _____ _____

GROWING UP IN A WORLD OF DARKNESS *(pages 304–317)*

Syllabication

A **syllable** is a word part with one vowel sound. If you are unsure of how to divide a word, look it up in the dictionary. Then say the syllables slowly and put them together.

A. Divide these words into syllables. Write each syllable on the line.

1. handicap   =   _____   +   _____   +   _____

2. relatives   =   _____   +   _____   +   _____

3. soundproof =   _____   +   _____

4. equipment =   _____   +   _____   +   _____

B. Separate these words from "Growing Up in a World of Darkness" into three syllables. Circle the syllable that gets the most stress when you say the word.

Word	1st Syllable	2nd Syllable	3rd Syllable
1. occasion			
2. instrument			
3. frustration			
4. popular			
5. studio			
6. introduce			

C. Complete each sentence with a word from Exercise B.

1. Stevie's first real musical _____ was a set of drums.

2. Songs are recorded in a special soundproof _____.

3. Many people enjoy listening to Stevie's music; it is very _____.

4. The audition at Hitsville USA was a special _____ for the whole family.

GROWING UP IN A WORLD OF DARKNESS (pages 304–317)

Words to Know

handicaps   encouraged   mimicking   self-conscious   audition

A. Fill in the blanks with the word from the list that best completes the sentence.

1. I wanted to be in the play, but first I had to show my skills in an _____.

2. Having _____ may make life difficult, but it doesn't prevent success.

3. I felt _____ because my parents supported me and told me to follow my dreams.

4. Ben felt very _____ because everybody stared at his bright clothing.

5. Sarah learned the dance steps by _____ and following the lead dancer.

B. Circle the letter next to the word that doesn't belong. Use the dictionary if necessary.

1. a. audition   b. perform   c. eat

2. a. nervous   b. self-conscious   c. confident

3. a. imitate   b. different   c. mimicking

4. a. encouraged   b. ignored   c. cheered

5. a. blind   b. handicaps   c. average

Writing Activity

Imagine you have lost one of your five senses: the ability to see, hear, touch, smell, or taste. How would this make your life different? Write four sentences using at least three of the **Words to Know.**

SOME PEOPLE *(pages 320–321)*

Theme

The **theme** of a poem is the idea about life that the writer wants to share with the reader. Read the following poem. Then answer the questions below.

You Whose Day It Is
—Native American

You whose day it is,

make it beautiful.

Get out your rainbow,

make it beautiful.

1. In lines 1–2, how does the speaker ask the reader to change the day?

   _____

2. What do you think the rainbow stands for in this poem?

   _____

3. Whose day is it?

   _____

4. What is this poem about?

   a. happiness   b. boredom   c. loneliness

5. What message or theme is the speaker sharing with the reader? Circle the letter beside the correct message.

   a. People should paint rainbows in order to be happy.

   b. Even if it rains, the day is filled with beauty because a rainbow might appear.

   c. Each day is a new day that you can make a good day.

ALMOST HUMAN *(pages 322–325)*

Speaker

Poets often imagine what it would be like to be someone or something else. They often write using the voice of another person or thing. The voice that talks to the reader in a poem is called the **speaker.** Reread the poem "Almost Human" and answer the following questions.

1. Which of the following details do we know about the speaker?

    a. The speaker is the poet.   b. The speaker is a person.

    c. The speaker is on vacation.   d. The speaker is a dolphin.

2. Whom is the speaker talking to?

    a. the people   b. the trainers   c. another dolphin   d. a child

3. What does the speaker say about people?

    a. People are easily trained.   b. The people are loud.

    c. The people are rude.   d. People look and dress funny.

4. What is humorous in the poem?

    a. The dolphins think people are trained.

    b. Dolphins can talk.

    c. People wave and clap.

    d. Dolphins dive and splash.

5. Why do you think the poet uses a dolphin as the speaker?

    a. To show that dolphins can speak to each other

    b. To show that dolphins are intelligent animals

    c. To make fun of people

    d. So that the reader can hear the dolphin's voice

POINT OF VIEW *(pages 326–327)*

Point of View

Besides choosing a speaker for their poetry, poets also decide from which point of view the poem will be told. **Point of view** refers to the way in which the poem is told. Poems can be told from the first-person or the third-person point of view.

I walked the dog this morning. (first-person)

She plays the drums. (third-person)

1. Look at lines 9–12 in the poem "Point of View." From which point of view is the poem told, first or third?

   _____

2. Name seven animals that the speaker talks about in the poem "Point of View."

   _____   _____

   _____   _____

   _____   _____

   _____

3. **Point of view** can also refer to the way a person or thing sees something. In "Point of View," the speaker tells how he or she feels about eating turkey, chicken, duck, and so forth. In the lines below, give the point of view of one of the animals in the poem.

   I am a _____.

   I am being eaten for _____.

   I feel _____.

   I wish I were _____.

NIKKI-ROSA *(pages 328–331)*

Free Verse

Poetry that does not have regular patterns of rhyme, rhythm, or line length is known as **free verse.** Notice the free verse poetry below. On the lines below the poem, break the sentences where you think each line should end. You do not have to use all the blank lines.

My true love's hair is black like shiny Sunday shoes.

It's short and stubborn, never obeys the comb.

_____

_____

_____

_____

_____

_____

_____

_____

On the lines below, write your own free verse poem. Choose an object in your classroom and write a poem about it. Use any of the five senses (seeing, hearing, tasting, smelling, touching) to describe the object.

_____

_____

_____

_____

_____

_____

_____

_____

_____

Vocabulary SkillBuilder

UNIT 10 POETRY *(pages 320–331)*

You read the following words in the poems in this unit. They are words you can learn.

shrivel *v.* dry up

communicate *v.* give information to another

respond *v.* act in return

biographers *n.* people who write the life stories of famous people

poverty *n.* the state of being poor

Write the correct word from the list above.

1. What is the opposite of wealth? _____

2. What is the opposite of grow? _____

3. When you become rich and famous, who will write about you? _____

4. What do people do when they speak and write? _____

5. If someone asks you a question, what should you do? _____

6. What do people do when they use a telephone? _____

7. People work hard for money to avoid living in what? _____

8. Who might write about a president? _____

9. Grapes do what to become raisins? _____

10. If you are invited to a party, what should you do? _____

THE INVADERS *(pages 334–339)*

Author's Purpose

The **author's purpose** is the reason why he or she writes a particular story or article. Authors write for many reasons.

Read each passage below. Then fill in the chart with the author's purpose. Choose from these purposes:
- to teach or inform
- to entertain
- to persuade the reader to think or act in a certain way
- to express the author's thoughts and opinions

Passage	Author's Purpose
1. In 1620 Miles Standish helped create the Plymouth Colony in Massachusetts. He became a leader of the group. Later, Standish, along with John Alden, helped start the town of Duxbury, Massachusetts.	
2. It makes me so angry when I think of how the Native Americans were treated by the European colonists. How could they have lied to and cheated the native people so cruelly? Must strong people always hurt those who are weaker than they are?	
3. Come see us at Plymouth Colony to find out how the Pilgrims survived during those first difficult years in the New World. You will learn a great deal about the American past from the friendly people of the colony. After you visit us, Thanksgiving will never be quite the same again.	
4. A flea and a fly in a flue Were imprisoned, so what could they do? Said the fly, "Let us flee." Said the flea, "Let us fly." So they flew through a flaw in the flue. —Anonymous	

THE INVADERS *(pages 334–339)*

Point of View

The **narrator** of a story is the person who is telling it. If the narrator is a character in the story, the story is told in the **first-person point of view.** The narrator uses pronouns such as *I* and *we.* If the narrator is outside the story, the story is told in the **third-person point of view.** The narrator uses pronouns such as *he, she,* and *they.*

A. Read each of these passages based on "The Invaders." Decide who is the speaker in each one; circle your answer. Then write whether the paragraph is written in the first-person or third-person point of view.

1. I met them first when I was almost a boy and I had been without caution. I approached them and they seemed friendly, but then suddenly they seized me and carried me off in their strange ship.

   Speaker: one of the invaders   the Native American   someone outside the story

   Point of view: _____

2. The invaders walked slowly through the forest. It had been a long journey to the New World. Some of the men were glad to be walking on solid ground after so many weeks at sea. But they were also cautious. No one knew if the natives in this land would be friendly or hostile.

   Speaker: one of the invaders   the Native American   someone outside the story

   Point of view: _____

3. I was greatly surprised when the native stepped out from the woods and said, "Welcome." Was it possible? Here, thousands of miles from England, a strangely dressed man was speaking to me in my own language. What a wonderful new land!

   Speaker: one of the invaders   the Native American   someone outside the story

   Point of view: _____

B. Rewrite this third-person sentence in the first-person point of view.

The Native American felt frightened when the invaders pointed their weapons at him.

_____

_____

THE INVADERS *(pages 334–339)*

Suffix *-ly*

A **suffix** is a word part added to the end of a word. The suffix *-ly* means "in a certain way." For example, *brightly* means "in a bright way." When adding *-ly* to a word ending in *y*, first change the *y* to *i* (example: *angry + -ly = angrily*).

A. Add the suffix *-ly* to each of the words below. Write the new word on the first line. Then write the meaning of the word on the second line.

1. cautious _____ _____

2. crazy _____ _____

3. pretty _____ _____

4. fervent _____ _____

5. silent _____ _____

6. cozy _____ _____

7. wary _____ _____

8. cruel _____ _____

B. Add a word that ends with the suffix *-ly* to complete each sentence. The meaning of the word is in parentheses.

1. The invaders walked _____ (in a slow way) through the forest.

2. The man hiding behind the tree watched them _____ (in a wary way).

3. The snow was falling _____ (in a light way).

4. If snow had been falling more _____ (in a heavy way), no one would have seen him run away.

5. The invaders had treated him _____ (in a cruel way) before.

6. The man was _____ (in a final way) sure that the invaders had come to stay.

7. He stepped forward _____ (in a bold way) and said

_____ (in a loud way), "Welcome."

THE INVADERS *(pages 334–339)*

Words to Know

craft   seized   exhibited   captive   savage

A. Circle the word or phrase that is most similar to the **boldfaced** word. Use a dictionary, if you need to.

1. I **exhibited** my art project in front of the rest of the class.

   a. made   b. presented   c. hid

2. I think it was cruel to hold the firefly **captive** in a glass jar.

   a. prisoner   b. king   c. comedian

3. The sailors boarded the **craft** and began their work.

   a. animal   b. ship   c. car

4. The lawyer called the criminal a **savage.**

   a. shy person   b. smart person   c. brutal person

5. The pirate **seized** the ship from the explorers.

   a. borrowed   b. captured   c. bought

B. Write **true** or **false** in the blanks.

_____ **1.** You can see a **craft** speeding down the highway.

_____ **2.** If you are **seized,** you have been taken by force.

_____ **3.** A painting in a museum is usually **exhibited** on the wall.

_____ **4.** A **captive** is a businessman.

_____ **5.** A **savage** would work well with others.

Writing Activity

Imagine you are stuck on a desert island. Write a note to send off in a bottle to rescuers. Use all of the **Words to Know.**

WEAPONS OF WAR *(pages 340–347)*

Compare and Contrast

When you **compare** two things, you look for ways in which they are alike. When you **contrast** them, you look for ways in which they are different.

A compare-and-contrast chart is a good way to show how things are alike and how they are different. Fill in the empty blocks in the chart below about the weapons described in "Weapons of War."

Weapon	Who used it	Why it was useful	Problems with it
Hunting rifle		Most men already had one.	
Musket	American and British soldiers	It could be fitted with a bayonet.	
Breech-loading rifle	American and British officers		There weren't enough for everyone to have one.
Saber	cavalrymen		
Tomahawk			To use one, you had to be very near the enemy.

Name_____

WEAPONS OF WAR *(pages 340–347)*

Patterns of Organization

Writers organize information to make it easier to understand and remember. One way to organize is by arranging facts and events in **chronological order,** or time order. Another pattern of organization is having all sentences in a paragraph or group of paragraphs relate to a **main idea.**

Read these parts of "Weapons of War." On the line, tell which pattern of organization the writer used—chronological order or main idea.

1. There were few cannons or other large weapons in America. Earlier fighting in the colonies had been against the Indians. Cannons did not roll well over the rough ground. They would not fit between the trees in the forests, where the Indians hid.

   This part of the article is organized using _____.

2. General Lee climbed into the *Turtle*. Quietly, he moved close to the warship. Now it was time to drill a hole just deep enough to hide a torpedo. He tried. But it wasn't working. "Why won't this work?" he wondered. "I just know this ship is made of wood!"

   This part of the article is organized using _____.

3. Muskets were loaded from the muzzle with the soldier standing up. After each shot, the man had to reload. The *flintlock* was a metal wheel that turned and set off sparks. The sparks lit the powder in the barrel of the gun. A soldier carried extra gunpowder and lead balls in a leather shoulder bag.

   This part of the article is organized using _____.

4. General Lee started back toward land. By now, sailors on the warship's deck had seen him. The sailors said, "What is that strange thing just under the water?" The *Eagle* sent out a small boat to see. Alarmed, Lee shot off a torpedo through the water. He did his best to aim it toward the ship. He missed the *Eagle*. But as the torpedo exploded, water flew high into the air. Men on all the nearby ships begin to shout and run about.

   This part of the article is organized using _____.

WEAPONS OF WAR *(pages 340–347)*

Context Clues: Definition Clues

Sometimes writers know that they are using many words in stories or articles that may be unfamiliar to their readers. To help readers, they provide **context clues** that tell the meaning of the unfamiliar words in the text. These clues are called **definition clues.**

A. Look for the definition clues. Write the definition of each **boldfaced** word on the line.

1. The **infantry**, that is, the soldiers on the front lines of battle, marched proudly.

   Infantry means _____.

2. At the end of each musket was a **bayonet,** which is a knife.

   A **bayonet** is _____.

3. The **flintlock** was a metal wheel that turned and set off sparks in the gun barrel.

   A **flintlock** was _____.

4. **Cavalrymen,** who were the soldiers who fought on horses, could move around the battlefield quickly and easily.

   Cavalrymen were _____.

5. The man inside the submarine turned a set of blades to make the sub move. In other words, he made a set of **propellers** go around.

   Propellers are _____.

B. Choose the correct word to complete each sentence.

flintlock   cavalrymen   infantry

1. The _____, that is, the soldiers on horseback, used sabers.

2. One of my ancestors was a member of the _____. In other words, he fought on foot in the front lines during the war.

3. The metal wheel that made sparks, which is called the _____, couldn't light the gunpowder if it got wet.

Name_____

WEAPONS OF WAR *(pages 340–347)*

Words to Know

tomahawks   torpedo   harbor   deck   anchors

A. Fill in each blank with the correct word from the list above.

1. Once the ship reached shore, the settlers dropped the _____ to keep the ship in one place.

2. _____ are tools very much like axes.

3. The sailors gathered together on the large _____ of the ship.

4. My father has a boat that he keeps at our town's _____.

5. My little brother ran around the house at full speed, pretending he was a

   _____ that could explode.

B. Use the **Words to Know** to fill in the blanks. Then use the boxed letters to complete the sentence below the puzzle.

1. What would you use to weigh down a ship?   __ __ __ __ __ __ [ ]

2. Native American peoples invented these.   __ __ __ [ ] __ __ __ __ __

3. This is home base for boats.   __ __ __ [ ] __ __

4. This is the main level on a ship.   __ [ ] __ __

5. This is an underwater weapon.   __ __ [ ] __ __ __ __

Answer the question with the word that the boxed letters spell out.

What is the name for the long, heavy weapon cavalrymen used? _____

Writing Activity
Write two sentences describing a boat of some kind. Use at least two of the **Words to Know.**

THE NEW MOTHER *(pages 348–363)*

Main Idea

The **main idea** is the most important idea in a paragraph. Sometimes a topic sentence states the main idea. Other sentences give details that tell more about the main idea.

A. Read this paragraph from "The New Mother." Then fill in the main idea diagram below. The top box contains the main idea of the paragraph. In the lower boxes, write details from the paragraph that tell more about the main idea.

> It was then that Sarah, peering through the gloom, saw the Lincoln children. They huddled on low stools near the fire, looking up at her out of frightened gray eyes. Sarah gasped at the sight of their thin, soiled clothing, their dark, matted hair, their pinched gray faces smudged with soot.

How the Lincoln children looked			

B. Read this paragraph from "The New Mother." Then fill in the main idea and the details in the diagram below.

> Most remarkable of all were the feather beds. One was laid on the pole bed in the corner. Another was placed on a clean bearskin in another corner to provide a sleeping place for the girls. The third was carried to the loft.

Main Idea:		
Detail 1:	Detail 2:	Detail 3:

THE NEW MOTHER *(pages 348–363)*

Historical Fiction

Historical fiction tells about real people or events and is set in the past. Like a nonfiction story, it has characters, a setting, and a plot.

A. Match the name of each character in "The New Mother" with his or her description.

1. _____ Sarah Lincoln		a.	a young man who lives with the Lincolns
2. _____ Tom Lincoln		b.	two friendly sisters
3. _____ Abe Lincoln		c.	a man who has married a new wife
4. _____ Dennis Hanks		d.	a shy, smart boy
5. _____ Sally		e.	a kind woman with plenty of energy
6. _____ Mathilda and Betsy		f.	a girl who is happy with her new mother

B. Cross out the phrase that is not a detail about the setting of "The New Mother."

a small cabin with a dirt floor   a clearing outside the cabin

a cornfield   a spring by the cabin

C. The six events below make up the plot of "The New Mother." In the blanks, write numbers to show the order of events.

_____ **1.** Sarah takes charge of the house.

_____ **2.** Abe acts shy around his new mother.

_____ **3.** Sarah gives Abe her books and he calls her Mamma.

_____ **4.** Sarah lets Abe read to her from her books.

_____ **5.** Sarah tells Abe that he is her boy and she'll help him all she can.

_____ **6.** Sarah meets Sally and Abe for the first time.

THE NEW MOTHER *(pages 348–363)*

Multiple-Meaning Words

When words have more than one meaning, we say they have **multiple meanings.** To understand the meaning the writer intended, think about how the word is used in context.

A. Read each sentence and the definitions for the underlined word. Then write the letter of the correct definition for each sentence.

1. _____ The crow found a <u>pitcher</u> with a little water in the bottom.

   a. in baseball, the player who throws the ball   b. container for liquids

2. _____ Abe and Mathilda started for the <u>spring</u>, swinging the water pail.

   a. flow of water from the ground   b. season that comes after winter

3. _____ Tom said, "You clean up your plate, or I'll give you a <u>hiding</u>."

   a. a beating   b. staying out of sight

4. _____ The crow could not get its <u>bill</u> into the pitcher for a drink.

   a. a bird's jaws and their covering   b. a written statement of amount owed

B. Choose the correct meaning for each underlined word in the sentences below.

1. _____ But Pappy says I already know how to read and write and <u>cipher</u>.

2. _____ The student wrote a <u>cipher</u> as the answer to the arithmetic problem.

   a. the symbol for zero   b. to solve arithmetic problems

3. _____ The museum has a picture of a wooly <u>mammoth</u>.

4. _____ The fireplace in the small cabin was <u>mammoth</u>.

   a. huge   b. an extinct elephant-like animal

5. _____ Sarah climbed the ladder to <u>peer</u> into the loft.

6. _____ A teenager prefers to shop with a <u>peer</u>.

   a. look   b. social equal

7. _____ Many hands make <u>light</u> work.

8. _____ I usually wear <u>light</u> colors when I walk at night.

   a. easy   b. not dark

THE NEW MOTHER (pages 348–363)

Words to Know

huddled   occurrence   astonishment   distress   reluctantly

A. In each blank, write the word from the list that best completes the sentence.

1. Although she didn't like it, the cat _____ allowed me to put her in the box.

2. There was a look of _____ on his face when everyone jumped up and yelled, "Surprise!"

3. We _____ together closely for warmth in the back seat of the car.

4. We have not had one _____ of cheating since the tests were put on a computer.

5. Laurence felt much _____ over the loss of his goldfish.

B. **Synonyms** are words that have nearly the same meaning. **Antonyms** are opposites. Beside each word, write a word from the list above that is **either** a synonym **or** an antonym for the word. Then circle "synonyms" or "antonyms" to describe the word pair.

1. event   _____ synonyms / antonyms

2. comfort   _____ synonyms / antonyms

3. surprise   _____ synonyms / antonyms

4. eagerly   _____ synonyms / antonyms

5. separated _____ synonyms / antonyms

Writing Activity
Write a paragraph about a major change in your life. Use at least two of the **Words to Know.**

THE BALLAD OF JOHN HENRY *(pages 364–369)*

Sequence

In stories, events are usually described in the order they happen. The writer tells what happens first, then second, and so on. This order is called **sequence.**

Fill in the following chart with events from the narrative poem "The Ballad of John Henry."

Box 1

At the age of three days, John Henry cries,

"_____

_____."

Box 2

The captain says that he is going to bring

_____.

Box 3

John Henry challenges the

_____

to a tunneling race.

Box 4

John Henry and

_____

begin hammering.

Box 5

John Henry drives his hammer

_____ feet and the

_____ drives only

_____ feet before it breaks.

Box 6

John Henry dies of

_____.

Box 7

People from the east and the west come to John Henry's funeral.

Box 8

Now, when people on a train pass John Henry's grave, they say,

"_____

_____."

THE BALLAD OF JOHN HENRY *(pages 364–369)*

Narrative Poetry

A **narrative poem** is a poem that tells a story. Like other stories, a narrative poem has characters, a setting, and a plot. A **ballad** is a type of narrative poem that is usually presented in the form of a song.

A. The main character in "The Ballad of John Henry" is John Henry himself. Answer these questions about John Henry.

  1. What is John Henry's reaction when the captain says that he is bringing a steam drill to do the job that John Henry had been doing?

  _____

  2. What happens to prove that John Henry gave everything he had in beating the steam drill?

  _____

  3. What can you tell about John Henry's character and personality from what he says and does?

  _____

B. Describe the setting of "The Ballad of John Henry." Where and when does the story take place?

  _____

  _____

C. Match each story event in Column 1 with a plot element in Column 2. Write the letter of the plot element before the event.

  Column 1   **Column 2**

  1. _____ John Henry dies.   a. introduction

  2. _____ John Henry predicts that a hammer will kill him.   b. rising action

  3. _____ Many people come to John Henry's funeral.   c. climax

  4. _____ John Henry races with the steam drill.   d. falling action

  5. _____ People remember John Henry as they pass his grave.   e. conclusion

FROM CALIFORNIA GOLD DAYS *(pages 370–379)*

Main Idea

The **main idea** is the most important idea in a paragraph. In some paragraphs, a **topic sentence** states the main idea. The topic sentence may be found anywhere in the paragraph.

A. Underline the topic sentence in each of these paragraphs.

1. The Forty-Niners made careful plans before starting. While waiting in the camps, parties and companies were formed. They agreed that it was safer to have ten to thirty wagons in a train. It would take about six yoke or pairs of oxen to each wagon. A captain would be the head of each party. He was to guide them over the plains and into California. Each man in the party was given certain duties.

2. The Indians did not bother the first parties. Those who came in 1850 had more trouble with them. But the Forty-Niners had other things to worry them. Many of the travelers became ill; some died. The wagons were much too heavy for hard travel. Many things were thrown away along the overland trail to make the wagons lighter. Others who came later could pick up what was needed along the way—if there was room to carry it. Most of the wagons were too loaded to carry anything more.

B. Choose the better topic sentence for each paragraph. Write the letter on the line.

1. _____. The men finished packing for the long journey and hitched up the oxen and mules. The women cooked, baked, and cared for the babies. The older children did chores for their parents.

   a. Even children were put to work.

   b. Everyone was busy now—men, women, and children.

2. One party was led by William Manly. Manly found a new map, but the map led through a terrible desert. The party had a very hard time and called the desert Death Valley.

   _____.

   a. That was a party that really made history.

   b. Manly had to go ahead to California and bring back food for the party.

FROM **CALIFORNIA GOLD DAYS** (pages 370–379)

Understanding Visuals

Visuals are drawings, pictures, charts, and maps that help readers understand the text.

Use the map from "California Gold Days" to fill in the chart below.

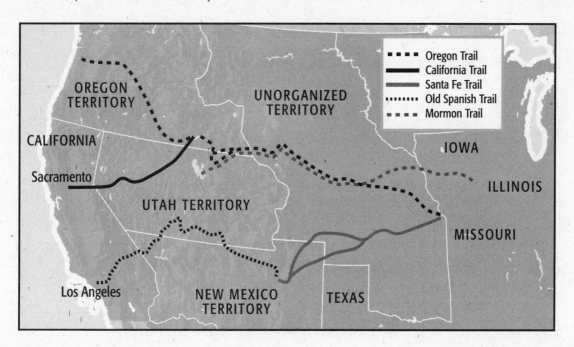

Read each description of the trails on the left. If the description matches the trail, put a check under the trail's name.

	Oregon Trail	California Trail	Santa Fe Trail	Mormon Trail	Old Spanish Trail
Goes to Salt Lake City					
Goes to Vancouver					
Ends in Sacramento					
Ends in Los Angeles					
Goes farthest north					
Goes farthest south					

FROM **CALIFORNIA GOLD DAYS** *(pages 370–379)*

Specialized Vocabulary

Every group of people who work or play together creates its own set of special words, or **specialized vocabulary** (also called jargon). Sometimes the people make up new words. At other times, they reuse old words and give them new meanings.

A. Unscramble the letters to find the word that matches each definition. Write the word on the blank.

1. people who headed west after gold was discovered in California

   y r F o t – i N e n r s   _____

2. the name given to any group of people who went west together

   t r p a y   _____

3. the person in charge of the group headed west

   n a c p i a t   _____

4. another name for a covered wagon (2 words)

   p e r a r i i   h o o s c e r n   _____   _____

5. a person who goes ahead to check for danger or the best way to go

   t o u s c   _____

B. Each underlined word is used in two different ways. Use context clues to choose the meaning that makes the most sense. Write the letter on the blank.

1. _____ The wagons were placed in a circle, <u>tongues</u> facing out.

   _____ When the <u>tongue</u> on my sneakers gets twisted, it hurts my foot.

   a. in shoemaking, the flap of material under the shoelaces

   b. the pole attached to the front of a horse-drawn vehicle

2. _____ When later <u>trains</u> came along, there was no grass for their oxen to eat.

   _____ A steam locomotive pulled the long freight <u>train</u> up the mountain.

   a. a group of railroad cars that run on tracks

   b. a group of covered wagons traveling together

3. _____ The most popular <u>fork</u> in the trail led to South Pass.

   _____ Why do I get the <u>fork</u> that is bent at every meal?

   a. a division into two or more branches   b. a utensil for eating foods

Words to Know SkillBuilder

Words to Know

plains   barrels   passes

A. Fill in each blank with the word from the list that best completes the sentence.

1. Our family drove through the _____ of the Great Smoky Mountains.

2. The circus uses _____ to hold food for the elephants.

3. You can find _____ in states that have much farmland. .

B. Complete the following analogies with the words from the list. Remember to say "Water is to lakes as grass is to *blank*."

1. WATER : LAKES :: grass : _____

2. _____ : mountains :: PATHS : PARKS

3. boxes: _____ :: FORKS : SPOONS

C. Using the Dictionary: Multiple Meanings

All three of the **Words to Know** are plural nouns. But if we drop the final **s,** they all have other meanings. Using your dictionary, fill in two definitions for each word.

plain:

barrel:

pass:

Writing Activity

Write a short paragraph telling whether you would have enjoyed traveling by wagon train to California. Use at least one of the **Words to Know.**

RABBIT FOOT: A STORY OF THE PEACEMAKER *(pages 380–385)*

Making Inferences

An **inference** is a guess that a reader makes, using clues from the story.

Read each set of clues from the story "Rabbit Foot." Underline the inference that makes more sense.

1. Many hundreds of years ago, before the Europeans came, the Five Nations of the Iroquois were always at war with one another.

    a. The Five Nations are still always at war.

    b. The Five Nations are no longer always at war.

2. The Great Creator sent a messenger named the Peacemaker.

    a. The Great Creator was angry with the warring tribes.

    b. The Great Creator cared about the tribes and wanted to help them.

3. The frog said, "Wa'he! That is so," when Rabbit Foot said that the snake really had him.

    a. The frog wasn't surprised to hear a human speak its language.

    b. The frog couldn't believe that a human was speaking to it.

4. Rabbit Foot suggested that the frog try to swallow the snake. Right away, the frog reached out and grabbed the snake's tail.

    a. The frog trusted Rabbit Foot.

    b. The frog feared Rabbit Foot as much as it feared the snake.

5. Both animals kept swallowing until nothing was left of either one.

    a. The animals were eager to make peace.

    b. Both animals were stubborn.

6. The Peacemaker said that the same thing would happen to the warring tribes unless they made peace.

    a. The Peacemaker believed the tribes would kill or destroy one another if they kept on fighting.

    b. The Peacemaker believed the tribes would eat one another unless they made peace.

RABBIT FOOT: A STORY OF THE PEACEMAKER *(pages 380–385)*

Theme

The **theme** of a story is the lesson it teaches about life, human nature, and how we should treat one another.

Read the events from "Rabbit Foot" in the outer circle below. Think about them and then write a possible theme for the story in the inner circle.

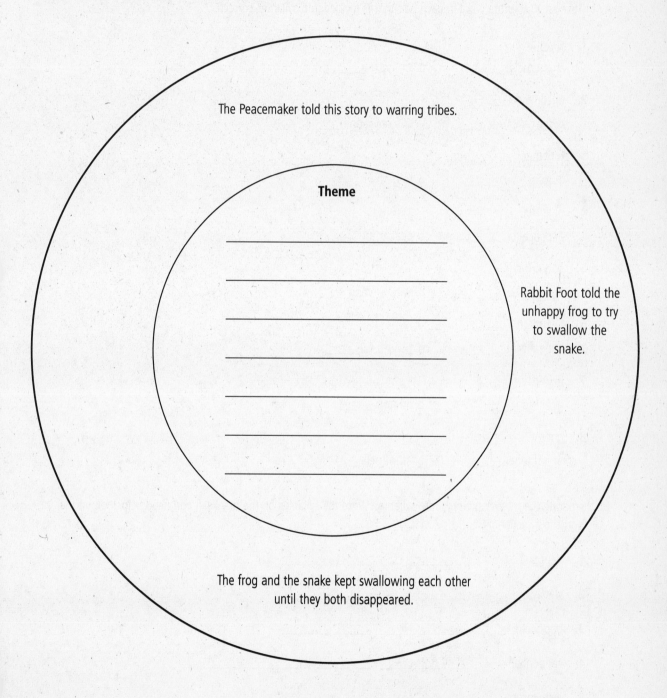

The Peacemaker told this story to warring tribes.

Theme

_____

_____

_____

_____

_____

_____

Rabbit Foot told the unhappy frog to try to swallow the snake.

The frog and the snake kept swallowing each other until they both disappeared.

RABBIT FOOT: A STORY OF THE PEACEMAKER *(pages 380–385)*

Syllabication

Syllables are word parts with one vowel sound each. Divide a word into syllables between consonants that come between two vowels (*rab-bit*); between the two words of a compound word (*camp-site*); after prefixes (*un-lock*); and before suffixes (*play-ful*). Do not separate the consonants in digraphs such as *ck, ch, sh,* and *th* (*au-thor*).

A. Make an **X** after the word in each pair that is divided into syllables correctly.

 1. struggle
      a. strug-gle _____   b. strugg-le _____

 2. uncommon
      a. un-comm-on _____   b. un-com-mon _____

 3. together
      a. to-get-her _____   b. to-geth-er _____

 4. peaceful
      a. peace-ful _____   b. peac-ef-ul _____

 5. swallowing
      a. swal-low-ing _____   b. swall-o-wing _____

 6. beautiful
      a. beaut-if-ul _____   b. beau-ti-ful_____

 7. hilltop
      a. hill-top _____   b. hil-ltop _____

 8. another
      a. a-not-her _____   b. an-oth-er ____

B. Separate the following words into syllables. Write the syllables on the blanks. If you need help, look up the words in a dictionary.

 1. happen   _____ - _____

 2. slowly   _____ - _____

 3. backward   _____ - _____

 4. cannonball   _____ - _____ - _____

 5. inchworm   _____ - _____

 6. distrustful   _____ - _____ - _____

RABBIT FOOT: A STORY OF THE PEACEMAKER *(pages 380–385)*

Words to Know

culture   feuds   coiled

A. Fill in each blank with the word from the list that best completes the sentence.

1. There are _____ that have existed between countries for hundreds of years.

2. I found the hose _____ up on the edge of the driveway.

3. Take pride in your _____; it's part of your identity.

4. I use my curling iron if I want my hair to be _____.

5. My mother was upset about the longtime _____ that went on in our family.

6. My parents and I travel a lot, so I get to experience much _____ from around the world.

B. Write **true** or **false** in each blank.

_____ **1.** A person's **culture** is his or her education.

_____ **2. Feuds** are bitter fights.

_____ **3.** Examples of things that are **coiled** are steps, walls, and roofs.

Writing Activity

Imagine you are a peacemaker. Write down a list of five ways in which you could keep peace between groups of people. Use at least one of the **Words to Know**.

from **HIROSHIMA** *(pages 388–404)*

Compare and Contrast

When you look for ways two things are alike, you are **comparing** them. When you look for ways two things are different, you are **contrasting** them.

Read the following list of details about the city of Hiroshima on August 6, 1945, and the Hiroshima of today. If a detail describes 1945 Hiroshima only, write it in the top circle. If the detail describes today's Hiroshima only, write it in the lower circle. If the detail describes both, write it in the space where the two circles overlap.

People fear American bombers.	Children go to school.
People see destruction.	There is a park where the bomb dropped.
People go shopping.	Paper cranes are hung.
There is a list of all those killed by the bomb.	A mushroom cloud rises above the city.

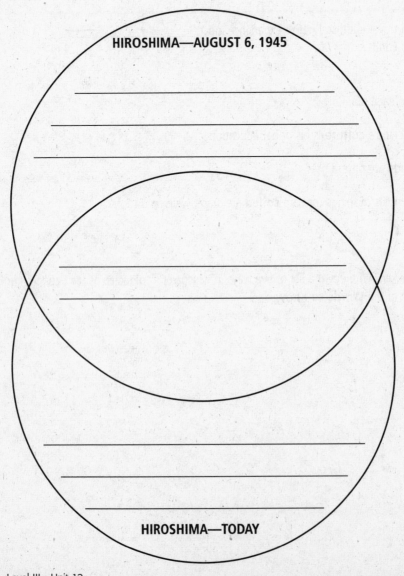

from HIROSHIMA *(pages 388–404)*

Plot

The **plot** is the set of events that make up a story. In some stories, two related plots take place at the same time. The first part of the excerpt from *Hiroshima*, for example, has two related plots. One plot describes the activities of the Japanese in the city. The other plot tells about the activities of the Americans in the bombers.

The time line below tracks events of both plots. Above the time line is a list of events involving Americans. Number the events in the order they happened, from A1 to A7. Below the time line is a list of events involving Japanese. Number the events in the order they happened, from J1 to J7. Answer the question below.

_____ A bomber called the *Straight Flush* flies above Hiroshima.

_____ The *Enola Gay* takes off from the island of Tinian.

__A7__ The Americans take pictures that record the effects of the explosion.

_____ The bomb explodes.

_____ The bombardier on the *Enola Gay* sees his target and releases the bomb.

_____ The *Straight Flush* tells the *Enola Gay* to continue to Hiroshima.

_____ A crewman sends a signal to the bomb that starts a chain reaction.

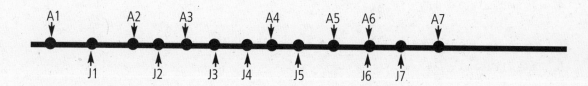

__J1__ People of Hiroshima start off to school and work.

_____ The people leave the bomb shelters and go back to their daily routines.

_____ An observer spots the *Enola Gay* nineteen miles east of Hiroshima.

_____ The people of Hiroshima experience the destruction caused by the bomb.

_____ Someone spots the *Straight Flush;* sirens send people into air-raid shelters.

_____ The bomb explodes.

_____ The people of Hiroshima look up and see the *Enola Gay.*

Which single event is the climax—the turning point—for both plots?

_____

_____

from **HIROSHIMA** *(pages 388–404)*

Latin Roots

Many words in the English language come from words in the Latin language. Knowing the meaning of Latin roots will help you understand many English words.

A. Each Latin word listed below is related to three English words in the box. Write each English word on the line after the related Latin word. Look for similarities in spelling and meaning.

radiant	corpse	office	bomb	million
bomber	radioactive	bombardier	millennium	corporation
officious	radiation	mile	corps	officer

1. *bombus,* "a deep, hollow sound"

   _____

2. *corpus,* "body"

   _____

3. *radius,* "spoke of a wheel"

   _____

4. *officium,* "service or duty"

   _____

5. *mīlle,* "thousand"

   _____

B. Choose from the words in Exercise A to complete these sentences.

1. The atom bomb put out rays, called _____, that caused death.

2. A plane that carries bombs is a _____.

3. After the bomb dropped, survivors tried to bury each dead body, or _____.

4. The duty of Colonel Tibbets was to be the _____ who piloted the *Enola Gay.*

5. The crew member called the _____ decides when to drop a bomb.

6. Anything that is _____ gives off energy in the form of rays.

7. The number shown by a one followed by six zeroes, which means a thousand thousand, is one

   _____.

8. Our _____ was originally based on a distance of a thousand steps.

from **HIROSHIMA** *(pages 388–404)*

Words to Know

routine   colonel   anxiously   devastated   radioactive

A. Fill in the blanks with the word from the list that best completes the sentence.

1. I _____ approached the principal's office.

2. The remains of the _____ village showed that a fire had destroyed the town.

3. The ride back and forth from school was a _____ trip.

4. We pretended our couch was a battlefield and the pillows were _____ missiles.

5. The _____ yelled at the officer because he had disobeyed orders.

B. Write **true** or **false** in the blanks.

_____ **1.** A **colonel** is the head librarian.

_____ **2.** If you **anxiously** wait for something, you are nervous.

_____ **3.** Something that is **radioactive** is against the law.

_____ **4.** Something that normally happens is **routine**.

_____ **5.** A city with crumbled buildings is **devastated**.

Writing Activity

The events in the excerpt from *Hiroshima* really happened. Using the true events, write about someone you make up who was in Hiroshima the day the atom bomb was dropped. Write at least one paragraph, and use at least three of the **Words to Know.**

from ANNE FRANK: CHILD OF THE HOLOCAUST *(pages 406–425)*

Patterns of Organization, Part I

A longer selection will often include more than one pattern of organization. Writers can organize information using an order that fits his or her material and purpose.

Read these passages from *Anne Frank: Child of the Holocaust*. Circle the pattern of organization that fits each passage.

1. In that year, the Great Depression began to spread through the United States and Europe. Stores closed, businesses failed, and many people lost their jobs. One out of every four persons in Frankfurt was unemployed. Those still working worried that they might be the next to become jobless.

    chronological order   compare and contrast   cause and effect

2. Anne's sister, Margot, got better grades in school and was the more serious of the two. Anne called her "brainy." Margot was well-behaved and kept her clothes and other things neat. Anne was messier with her belongings. She also had high spirits.

    compare and contrast   main idea and details   cause and effect

3. Jews got the worst treatment in Germany. They could no longer hold government jobs. All Jewish officials, like the mayor of Frankfurt, had to resign. Non-Jewish Germans were ordered not to go to Jewish doctors or hire Jewish lawyers. In the schools, Jewish students were segregated—put in separate classes. Jewish teachers were fired.

    cause and effect   chronological order   main idea and details

4. In 1938, all Jewish students were ordered out of German schools. At the end of that year, the Nazis staged mass arrests of Jews, sending 30,000 to concentration camps. They also encouraged mobs to attack Jews throughout the country—in their homes, shops, and synagogues.

    main idea and details   chronological order   cause and effect

5. Most of the Jews still living in Germany could have been saved, but many couldn't leave. They had nowhere to go. Other countries, including the Netherlands and the United States, only took in a certain number of new people from other nations. They might bend the rules a little for those who were in danger, like the German Jews, but not much.

    compare and contrast   main idea and details   cause and effect

from ANNE FRANK: CHILD OF THE HOLOCAUST *(pages 406–425)*

Patterns of Organization, Part II

A single paragraph should follow a single **pattern of organization,** such as chronological order (also called *sequence*), or main idea and details. However, a longer piece of writing often combines several passages with different organizations.

Read these passages from *Anne Frank: Child of the Holocaust.* Tell how each is organized—by **chronological order** or by **main idea and details.**

1. Why would anyone want to read about the most private thoughts of a 13-year-old girl? That's what Anne Frank asked herself as she wrote in her dairy in the early 1940s. She was, after all, an ordinary 13-year-old. Her parents didn't seem to understand her. She often couldn't figure out the boys she knew. And she did not care for some of her teachers.

   This paragraph of the article is organized using _____.

2. In 1925, Otto married Edith Hollander, whose family was also in business. Their first daughter, Margot, was born the next year. Anne was born in 1929.

   This paragraph of the article is organized using _____.

3. Like other young men his age, Otto served in the German army during World War I. He joined in 1915, became an officer, and won several medals. After the war, he went into business for himself.

   This paragraph of the article is organized using _____.

4. By the time she was in grade school, Anne had many friends. Anne and her friends liked to play pingpong and a game similar to hopscotch. The also did handstands against the wall in a nearby playground.

   This paragraph of the article is organized using _____.

from ANNE FRANK: CHILD OF THE HOLOCAUST *(pages 406–425)*

Context Clues

To figure out the meaning of a new word, look for clues in its context—that is, the words and phrases around the word. A **definition clue** directly states the meaning of the word. A **contrast clue,** like an antonym, tells what is not meant.

A. Use definition and contrast clues to figure out the meaning of the **boldfaced** words. Write the meanings.

1. In contrast to many people in Frankfurt who were **unemployed,** Otto Frank had a job.

    Unemployed means _____.

2. In Nazi Germany, Jewish students were **segregated,** that is separated, from other students.

    Segregated means _____.

3. Anne Frank was very talkative, but her sister Margot was **reserved.**

    Reserved means _____.

4. The Jews had a **curfew.** A curfew is a time after which certain people are not allowed on the streets.

    A **curfew** is _____.

5. The Franks were in **jeopardy**—danger—of being sent to concentration camps.

    Jeopardy means _____.

B. Use a **boldfaced** word from Exercise A to finish each sentence below.

1. The night before the championship game, the football team had a _____ of 9:00.

2. Years ago, the people who had smallpox were _____ from healthy people in order to stop the spread of the disease.

3. When the factory closed, many workers became _____.

4. Because of the heavy rain, the town was in _____ of being flooded.

5. Emily was a quiet, _____ little girl.

Name_____

from ANNE FRANK: CHILD OF THE HOLOCAUST *(pages 406–425)*

Words to Know

tolerant   secure   synagogues   torture

A. Fill in the blanks with the word from the list that best completes the sentence.

1. Once we were in bed, we felt safe and _____.

2. The thought of going to school all year round seems like _____.

3. Christians attend churches; Jews attend _____.

4. My parents have taught me to be _____ of other beliefs and religions.

B. Choose the word or phrase that is most similar to the **boldfaced** word. Use the dictionary if you need to.

1. I felt more **secure** walking with my brother.
   a. embarrassed   b. scared   c. safe

2. We attended services at two different **synagogues.**
   a. Jewish places of worship   b. Catholic places of worship   c. Muslim places of worship

3. Jane said she would be strong enough to withstand **torture.**
   a. pain as punishment   b. exercise   c. rejection

4. Remaining **tolerant** of your fellow human beings is the key to peace.
   a. unfriendly   b. respectful   c. uncaring

Writing Activity

What did you find disturbing about this biography of Anne Frank? Write two or three sentences, using at least two of the **Words to Know.**

BLACK WHITENESS *(pages 426–449)*

Cause and Effect

Events in a story are related by cause and effect. The **cause** explains why the event occurred. The **effect** tells what happened.

Fill in the boxes to show causes and effects in "Black Whiteness."

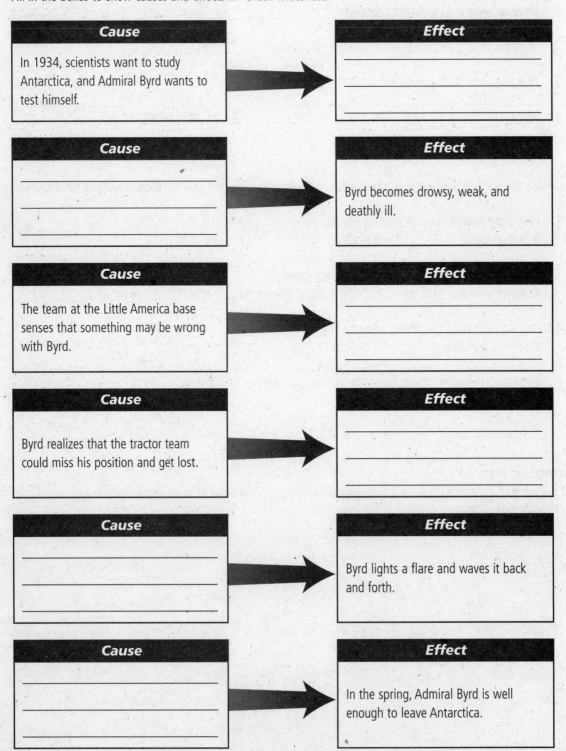

Cause	Effect
In 1934, scientists want to study Antarctica, and Admiral Byrd wants to test himself.	_____ _____ _____
_____ _____ _____	Byrd becomes drowsy, weak, and deathly ill.
The team at the Little America base senses that something may be wrong with Byrd.	_____ _____ _____
Byrd realizes that the tractor team could miss his position and get lost.	_____ _____ _____
_____ _____ _____	Byrd lights a flare and waves it back and forth.
_____ _____ _____	In the spring, Admiral Byrd is well enough to leave Antarctica.

BLACK WHITENESS *(pages 426–449)*

Figurative Language

Figurative language helps readers form vivid pictures in their minds. Both metaphors and similes compare things that seem different. **Similes** use *like* or *as* in the comparison; **metaphors** say that one thing is the other. **Personification** gives human qualities to ideas or nonliving things.

A. Answer each question about figurative language in "Black Whiteness."

1. Outside, Admiral Byrd's breath hangs above his head like a small cloud.

    Byrd's breath is compared to _____.

    How are these two things alike? _____

2. The cold in the little room lies like a thick liquid.

    The cold is compared to _____.

    How are these two things alike? _____

3. The snow is rough and brittle as white sandstone.

    The snow is compared to _____.

    How are these two things alike? _____

4. The flare makes a huge blue hole in the night.

    The flare is compared to _____.

    How are these two things alike? _____

5. July is "born in cold."

    How is July made to seem alive? _____

6. The kite skates to a height of over a hundred feet.

    How is the kite made to seem human? _____

B. Complete each sentence with your own figurative language.

1. In the quiet cabin, the ticking of the clock sounded as loud as _____.

2. Huge snowflakes _____ along the rooftop.

3. During the Antarctic winter, the darkness is _____.

BLACK WHITENESS *(pages 426–449)*

Prefixes

Prefixes are word parts added to the beginning of a base word. Knowing the meaning of common prefixes helps a reader figure out unfamiliar words.

Prefix	Meaning
dis-	opposite of
mis-	wrong; incorrectly
mid-	middle part of
un-	not
re-	again; back

A. Write the meaning of each of these words from "Black Whiteness." Use the chart above to help you.

1. disappear _____

2. regain _____

3. unknowing _____

4. midafternoon _____

5. misspelled _____

B. Complete each of the following sentences with a word from the list below.

retrace   unbelievable   misspelling   disagree   midstream

1. Admiral Byrd's story of spending months living alone in the Antarctic is not easy to believe;

   instead, it is almost _____.

2. If you go off the marked path in the Antarctic wilderness, it is very hard to find your way back,

   or _____ your steps.

3. The tractor team could get stuck _____, that is, in the middle of the frozen river.

4. This newspaper article called the great explorer "Admiral Bird," but that mistake was a

   _____.

5. Scientists do not always share the same opinion about exploring the Antarctic; sometimes they

   _____ about it.

Name_____

BLACK WHITENESS *(pages 426–449)*

Words to Know

aluminum   cringe   paralysis   nausea   circulation

A. Fill in the blanks with the word from the list that best completes the sentence.

1. My father couldn't move his legs; he suffered _____.

2. Therese lost _____, or the movement of blood, in her foot from sitting on it.

3. The trash can was made from shiny _____.

4. Fingernails on a blackboard make my nerves tingle, and I _____.

5. A wave of _____ came over me; my stomach revolted when I

smelled the rotting food.

B. Use the clues below and the words from the list to fill in the puzzle.

Across

2. cans are made of this

4. sick stomach

5. flow of blood

Down

1. shrink back

3. loss of power to move

Writing Activity

Imagine you are on a journey. Write a journal entry describing a life-threatening experience you have on this journey. Use at least one of the **Words to Know.**

Writing Prompts

Writing Templates

Revising and Editing Tips

Writing Prompts

Unit 1 Not According to Plan

1. The Tell-Tale Heart *pages 4–13*

The "Tell-Tale Heart" is a horror tale. In your opinion, is the story scary? What kinds of reactions did you have to the thoughts and actions of the narrator? What parts of the story do you think were intended to create a scary response?

Write your opinion of "The Tell-Tale Heart." Use details from the story to support your opinion.

2. Cinder Edna *pages 14–25*

In "Cinder Edna," the character Cinder Edna is described as "spunky." This means she has spirit or courage. What other qualities do you think Cinder Edna shows in the fairy tale?

Write a short character description of Cinder Edna. Be sure to include details from "Cinder Edna" that show examples of her other qualities.

3. The No-Guitar Blues *pages 26–37*

Fausto of "The No-Guitar Blues" does get a guitar after all. However, he never solves the problem of finding work when he needs extra money.

Write a how-to paragraph that explains a few ideas to Fausto about earning money. Think about the ways he tries and fails to find work. How might he find a job that he can do on a regular basis?

UNIT 1 WRITING ASSIGNMENT: SHORT STORY

Recall such expressions as "When the going gets tough, the tough get going" or "no pain—no gain." Write a short story that shows how a character deals with an unexpected turn of events. Use the template on the next page to help you organize your story.

Short Story

Characters:

Setting:

Basic conflict:

Background:

Event 1:

Event 2:

Event 3:

Turning point:

Resolution:

Revising and Editing

Revising Skill: Show, Don't Tell

Bring your writing to life! To capture your readers' attention, use details to show what happens. Which sentence shows rather than just tells?

A. The coins fell into the collection plate.

B. The coins clinked as they struck the sides of the brass collection plate.

Change the sentences below, so that they show instead of tell.

1. Fausto got a quarter going to the store.

_____

_____

2. Roger's owners had a nice kitchen.

_____

_____

3. Fausto tore his pants playing football.

_____

_____

Editing Tip: Punctuating Dialogue

If you include dialogue in your short story, be sure to put whatever your characters say in quotation marks. When a second person begins speaking, start a new paragraph with a new set of quotation marks.

Example:

When the basketball game had ended and the players were about to leave the court, Cody asked, "Where's my jacket?"

"I thought you left it back in your locker," answered Phil. Then he looked at the nearest bench on the court.

Revise Your Short Story

Now go back to your short story. Make sure your details are interesting so they show rather than tell. Check to see that you've placed quotation marks correctly around the dialogue and that readers can tell which character is saying what.

Writing Prompts

Unit 2 Courage Counts

1. A Slave *pages 40–47*

According to this true account, messages about "Friends across the Ohio River" had begun to reach the slaves on Southern plantations. They were hearing phrases such as *"Look for the lantern!"* and *"Listen for the bell!"*

Write a paragraph to explain how hearing about the Underground Railroad might have given a fearful slave a sense of hope.

2. Wilma Mankiller *pages 48–59*

In the biography, you read that Wilma Mankiller faced two conflicts as a person in a public role. She had to deal with her shyness. She also had to deal with those who believed a woman should not be a leader in the Cherokee Nation.

In a sentence or two, explain which conflict you think was easier for Wilma Mankiller to overcome. Find reasons in the biography to support your explanation.

3. Cesar Chavez: Civil-Rights Champion *pages 60–67*

To fight for the rights of workers, Cesar Chavez used a number of nonviolent tactics. The biography "Cesar Chavez: Civil-Rights Champion," shows that he used these tactics even when his followers wanted to try other ways to reach their goals.

In your opinion, what made Cesar Chavez an effective leader? Write your opinion and include evidence from the biography.

4. Roberto Clemente: Hero and Friend *pages 68–77*

This biography gives many details about the life of Roberto Clemente and the dream he had to help others.

Write a brief tribute to Roberto Clemente. Explain why he was considered a hero both on and off the baseball field.

UNIT 2 WRITING ASSIGNMENT: ESSAY

What pet peeve do you have about your neighborhood or school? What steps or decisions do you think could help solve the problem? Tackle the issue by writing a problem-solution essay. To gather and develop ideas, use the template on the following page.

Problem-Solution Essay

Problem:

Possible Solutions	Results—Pros and Cons
1.	Pro Con
2.	Pro Con

Decision:

Revising Skill: Using Examples and Facts

How do you make writing that is about real things clear and interesting? Including examples and facts is one way. The reader gets a better picture of what you are talking about. In the sentence below, the writer gives an example of a *skiff*.

It took the slave owner time to locate a skiff, but a small boat was found at last.

Use the facts and examples in the chart to revise the sentences below.

Facts about Cesar Chavez	Examples of Roberto Clemente's skills
1. born in 1927 2. served in the Navy	5. ran the 60-yard dash in 6.4 seconds. The world record was 6.1 seconds. • batted .414, hit 2 home runs, and had 12 hits and 4 runs batted in

1. Chavez was born a long time ago. *(Use a fact.)*

   _____

2. Chavez served in the military. *(Use a fact.)*

   _____

3. Clemente was fast. *(Use an example.)*

   _____

4. Clemente was the Most Valuable Player in the 1971 World Series. *(Use an example.)*

   _____

   _____

Quick-Fix Editing Machine p. 206

Editing Tip: Consistent Verb Tense
Be sure to use the same verb tense for all things that happen during the same time.

Incorrect: Wilma looked and see the tall buildings.

Correct: Wilma looked and saw the tall buildings.

Revising Your Problem-Solution Essay
As you revise your essay add facts and examples to help make it clear and interesting. Check your sentences for consistent verb tenses.

Writing Prompts

Unit 3 We Are Family

1. Trombones and Colleges *pages 80–89*

In "Trombones and Colleges," Clyde's mother is disappointed about Clyde's report card. Instead of scolding Clyde, she shares a memory of how Clyde's father learned how to do something that was very hard for him to do well at first.

What kind of parent would tell such a story? Write a brief character sketch of Clyde's mother. Include details that show certain personal qualities she has.

2. In a Neighborhood in Los Angeles *pages 90–93*

"In a Neighborhood in Los Angeles" is a poem in which a speaker describes his grandmother. What if the poem had been about the grandson and the grandmother had been the speaker?

Imagine that you're another member of the speaker's family. Write a thank-you note to express how touched you were by the memories the speaker shared in the poem.

3. Mudslinging *pages 94–97*

The article "Mudslinging" shows one way families can come together to prevent problems.

Write a persuasive paragraph to convince readers that in family relationships, closeness is better than conflict.

4. Another April *pages 98–112*

In "Another April," a grandfather takes a walk on a cold, spring day, determined to find an old friend. Grandpa's friend is a terrapin with the date 1847 carved into its shell.

Write a comparison-and-contrast paragraph that describes how Grandpa and the terrapin are alike and different. Use descriptions from the story to help you.

UNIT 3 WRITING ASSIGNMENT: CHARACTER SKETCH

This unit features several characters with close family connections. Choose one of the characters and write a character sketch. Show what matters to that character about his or her family relationships. Filling in the template on the next page will help you write your character description.

Character Sketch

Character's name and relation:	My response:

Details: how the character looks

Details: what the character says

Details: what the character does

Details: how others react

Conclusion:

Revising Skill: Adding Details

Details make your writing lively and appealing. Which sentence is more interesting?

> The musician played the trombone loudly.
>
> The musician blasted the trombone and filled the room with a soulful song.

1. Clyde put his backpack on the table and sat down. *(Tell what kind of backpack Clyde had and how he sat.)*

   _____

   _____

   _____

2. The family members in the yard were throwing mud. *(Tell the number of family members, and describe the yard and the mud.)*

   _____

   _____

   _____

3. To prepare for the weather Grandpa wore a cap and a suit. *(Tell what kind of weather it was and describe Grandpa's cap and suit.)*

   _____

   _____

   _____

Quick-Fix Editing Machine p. 202

Editing Tip: Pronoun References

To make sure your sentences are clear, check to see that the pronouns you use agree in number with their antecedents.

Incorrect: Every math problem has their steps.

Correct: Every math problem has its steps.

Revise Your Character Sketch

Look over the character sketch you wrote. Does the sketch include your response to the character? Does it include details about how the character looks and what the character says and does? Make sure the pronouns you've used in the sketch refer clearly to their antecedents.

Writing Prompts

Unit 4 Who's in Charge?

1. The Telephone *pages 116–127*

In a play, the characters' words, or dialogue, are spoken by actors on a stage. *The Telephone* is a play that is a mystery. In the play, Victor is trying to get his dead uncle Jonathan's money. Why does Victor want Uncle Jonathan's money?

Have Victor tell why he wants Uncle Jonathan's money. Write what Victor says as dialogue.

2. The Prince and the Pauper *pages 128–157*

In the play *The Prince and the Pauper,* two boys trade places. One is a king, and the other a poor boy, a pauper. Which boy would you rather be in real life: the prince—with a life of privilege—or the pauper—with a life of freedom and rowdy mischief?

Write a paragraph explaining which way of life you would like and why. Give reasons from the play to tell why you think one way of life would be better.

UNIT 4 WRITING ASSIGNMENT: COMPARISON-AND-CONTRAST ESSAY

Write a comparison-and-contrast essay that describes how the two boys in The Prince and the Pauper are alike and how they are different. Use the template on the next page to help you write your essay. In the first box, list two features to be compared, such as dress, lifestyle, family, or friends. Label them 1 and 2. Then tell what you want to find out by making this comparison. For Feature 1, describe the prince as Subject A and the pauper as Subject B. Do the same for Feature 2. In the next box tell how the prince and the pauper are similar and how they are different. Then write your conclusion. It should tell what you found out as a result of the comparison.

Comparison-and-Contrast Essay (by Feature)

Features being compared:

Reasons for comparison:

Feature 1

Subject A	Subject B

Feature 2

Subject A	Subject B

Similarities/Differences:

Conclusion:

Revising Skill: Pronoun Case

In a story, the writer varies the use of names and pronouns. Varying names and pronouns creates rhythm and makes the writing smooth and interesting. The writer must use the right pronoun case to keep his or her writing clear and correct. Which sentence is correct?

A. Jay and me are often mistaken for twins.

B. Jay and I are often mistaken for twins.

Rewrite the sentences. Change the underlined words to pronouns. Be sure to use the correct pronoun case.

1. No, Mildred, <u>Victor</u> must wait a little longer.

_____

2. I am delighted with <u>Jonathan</u>.

_____

3. "<u>The Guards</u> will not believe me when I tell them about this," said the prince.

_____

_____

4. Tom said, "The king will come looking for <u>Tom and Edward</u> soon."

_____

_____

Quick-Fix Editing Machine p. 206

Editing Tip: Consistent Verb Tense
Keep verb tenses the same within a sentence or paragraph.

Incorrect: After the grand ball ended, the queen goes upstairs.

Correct: After the grand ball ended, the queen went upstairs.

Revise Your Paragraph
Now look back at the paragraph you wrote. Be sure that you used pronouns correctly. Check your verb tenses to make sure they are the same.

Writing Prompts

Unit 5 Special Places

1. Elevator *pages 162–163*

In the poem "Elevator," a person waits and reads. Where do you often have to wait for something to start? What do you do while waiting?

Write a paragraph telling where you spend time waiting, whether it's standing in line or sitting in a waiting room. Tell what you do while waiting. Describe how waiting makes you feel.

2. Happy Thought *pages 166–167*

The happy thought in the poem "Happy Thought" makes the poet smile, laugh, and giggle. What does a happy thought do to you?

Write one stanza of a poem telling what your happy thoughts make you do. Tell how you show that you are happy.

3. Daybreak in Alabama *pages 168–169*

The poem "Daybreak in Alabama" gives the reader a vivid picture of what Alabama is like. What state or city could you describe?

Write a paragraph describing a state or city that you know well. Use vivid words to describe the things you like about your state or city.

UNIT 5 WRITING ASSIGNMENT: POEM

Write a poem using sensory words to describe a happy place that you have been to or an event you have attended. For example, you might describe a noisy concert or a quiet pond. Describe details that you can see, smell, hear, taste, or feel. Use the template on the next page to help you write your poem. Write the name of the place in the subject circle. Then use the other circles to tell about it.

Cluster Diagram for Poem

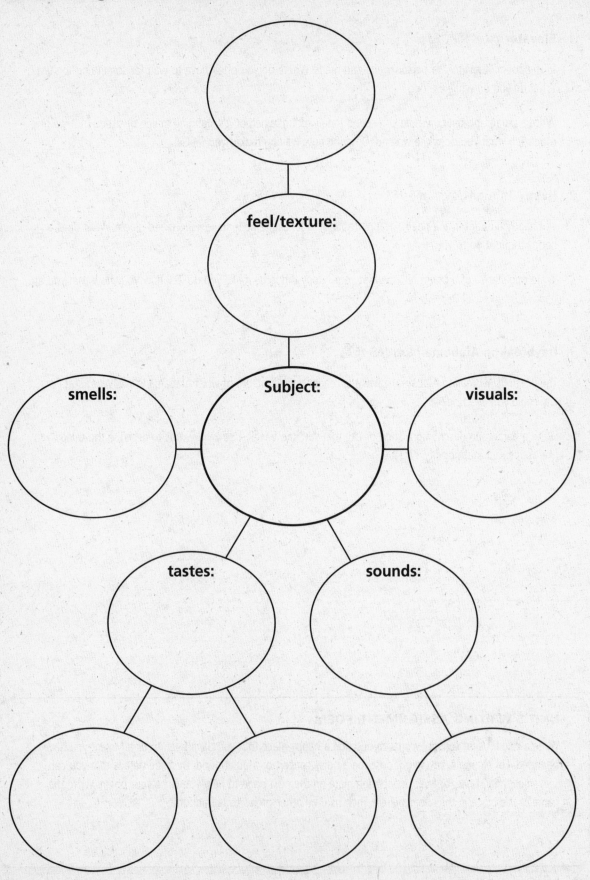

Revising and Editing

Revising Skill: Using Sensory Images

Sensory images are pictures in your mind. Sensory imagery in poetry helps you use your senses to picture things. You can almost use your senses to see, smell, hear, taste, or touch the pictures in your mind. Which words help you see things in your mind?

> She slipped and fell on the cold, wet grass and landed face down—salty, slippery mud landed in her mouth.

Write three sentences. Use sensory imagery to help readers see things in their minds.

1. Use sight and smell.

_____

_____

2. Use sound and feeling.

_____

_____

3. Use taste.

_____

_____

Editing Tip: Punctuating Poetry

Poets may punctuate their poems however they want. In general, they use punctuation marks to make sure their poems are read correctly. Poets want readers to pause at the right spots. Generally, use standard rules for punctuating your poems to help the reader understand your ideas. Use end marks after full sentences, and use commas in the correct way.

Avoid: Shadows creep crawl
    slide across my wall

Better: Shadows creep, crawl
    slide across my wall

Revise Your Poem

Now go back to the poem you wrote. Add sensory images to help the reader make pictures in his or her head. Make sure that the punctuation makes sense and helps the reader say the poem aloud.

Writing Prompts

Unit 6 The Battle Is On!

1. High as Han Hsin *pages 176–189*

Not every smart person looks smart. In "High as Han Hsin," Han Hsin survives because other people misjudge his looks and actions.

Write a persuasive argument to support the idea that appearances can fool others. Use examples from "High as Han Hsin" to support this view.

2. For Want of a Horseshoe Nail *pages 190–193*

In this work of historical fiction, a kingdom is lost because a small thing wasn't done.

In a brief paragraph, explain what lesson you think the writer of this story wants readers to understand. Or explain why this story has personal meaning for you.

3. Shot Down Behind Enemy Lines *pages 194–203*

This true account describes both the physical and mental challenges Captain Roger Locher faced in trying to stay alive in a jungle.

Imagine that you are making a short speech at a medal-pinning ceremony for the rescued captain. Focus on how Locher showed determination and courage. Include details from the account.

4. Fa Mulan *pages 204–213*

In this legend, a soldier tells Fa Mulan, "You excel because you balance male and female energies."

In a brief comparison-and-contrast paragraph, write what traits or abilities Fa Mulan has that set her apart from all the other warriors. Be sure to mention specific examples from the legend.

UNIT 6 WRITING ASSIGNMENT: COMPARISON-AND-CONTRAST ESSAY

Choose any two warriors from this unit. Write a comparison-and-contrast essay that shows each warrior's fighting situation, how he or she faces it, and the result. To help you see differences and similarities clearly as you develop ideas, use the template on the next page. Label one warrior as Subject A and the other as Subject B. In the next box tell what you want to find out as a result of the comparison. Then describe two things/features about each warrior. Then tell how they are alike and different. Last, write your conclusion. It should tell what you found out as a result of the comparison.

Comparison-and-Contrast Essay (by Subject)

Subjects being compared:

Reasons for comparison:

Subject A

Feature 1

Feature 2

Subject B

Feature 1

Feature 2

Similarities/Differences:

Conclusion:

Revising Skill: Fixing Errors in Reasoning

When you want readers to fully understand and accept the ideas you present in your writing, keep your statements clear. Try to avoid making errors in reasoning. Here are two kinds of errors.

An overgeneralization usually includes words like *everyone, always, none, all.* Anyone who enjoys action movies likes exciting battle scenes.	**Correct Reasoning** Many who enjoy action movies like exciting battle scenes.
A false cause and effect is the mistaken idea that one event causes another. I tripped over the curb because it's in the wrong place.	**Correct Reasoning** I tripped over the curb because I wasn't watching what I was doing.

Rewrite these statements to fix errors in reasoning.

1. Han Hsin would not have invented the kite if he had been able to hold the prince's spear.

_____

_____

2. No king can win a battle by listening to a groom.

_____

_____

3. Fa Mulan shows that all women make excellent warriors.

_____

_____

Quick-Fix Editing Machine p. 200

Editing Tip: Subject-Verb Agreement
When a subject and a verb are both singular or both plural, they agree. Be sure the subjects and verbs in your sentences agree in number.

Incorrect: Mulan's companions was surprised to discover her secret.

Correct: Mulan's companions were surprised to discover her secret.

Revise Your Comparison-and-Contrast Essay
Check your essay to make sure your comparisons or contrasts are clear. Check that your statements are sound and don't seem too broad or unreasonable. Check for agreement in number of your subjects and verbs.

Writing Prompts

Unit 7 Decisions Don't Come Easily

1. Two Were Left *pages 216–221*

Should Noni, cold and starving, have struggled so much over the decision to keep his dog Nimuk alive? Should Noni have been more fearful of what his dog might do?

Write your opinion of Noni's actions. Give reasons for your opinion.

2. Terrible Things: An Allegory of the Holocaust *pages 222–230*

An allegory is a story whose characters and events stand for something else. In general, the Terrible Ones stand for groups that use fear to divide and destroy others. The forest animals stand for human beings who recognize the growing danger and react in different ways.

Write about what the story means. Be sure to include details from the story to support your statements about it.

3. The Lady, or the Tiger? *pages 232–241*

For decades, "The Lady, or the Tiger?" has puzzled readers because the writer ended it with a question instead of an answer. The writer left you to decide what door the young man chose.

Decide! Write your own ending that reveals the young man's choice.

UNIT 7 WRITING ASSIGNMENT: OPINION STATEMENT

In the stories of this unit, certain characters or groups face difficult choices. Which character, in your opinion, is the bravest? Write an opinion statement. The template on the following page can help you gather and record evidence to support your opinion.

Opinion Statement

State Opinion:

Reason 1: Supporting Evidence

Reason 2: Supporting Evidence

Reason 3: Supporting Evidence

Conclusion:

Revising Skill: Coherence

A **paragraph** is coherent when all its sentences are related and follow an order. Your paragraphs will be easier to understand if you put events in order and use transition words. Which paragraph is coherent?

A. The Terrible Things came for the birds. They came for the squirrels. They came for the frogs, the fish, and the porcupines. They came for the rabbits.

B. **First,** the Terrible Things came for the birds. **Next,** they came for the squirrels. **Then** they came for the frogs, the fish, and the porcupines. **Finally,** they came for the rabbits.

Rewrite the following paragraph to make it coherent. Use transition words or phrases such as *first, next, then, last, During the same time.*

The princess learns the secret of what is behind which door. The king arrests the servant. The princess makes a motion to the right. The king sets a trial date for the servant. The servant chooses a door.

_____

_____

_____

_____

_____

_____

_____

Editing Tip: Paragraphing

When a paragraph contains too many ideas, readers get confused or lose interest. When the main idea of your paragraph changes, start a new paragraph. Notice the mark to start a new paragraph in the text below.

I think the servant chose the door that has the tiger behind it. The princess was too jealous. She didn't want him to choose the door with the lady. He didn't know it but he had no way out. ⁋ It was surprising to me that the story ends the way it does. I was expecting the writer to tell everything.

Revise Your Opinion Statement

Take a close look at your opinion statement. Have you stated your position clearly and used facts to support it? Are your paragraphs coherent? Do your paragraphs start and end where they make the most sense?

Writing Prompts

Unit 8 Hard to Believe

1. **Ships That Could Think** *pages 244–251*

   "Ships That Could Think" is an informative article that tries to explain two mysterious incidents involving ships. Articles like this often appear in magazines that people read for information or entertainment.

   Write an explanation of why you think articles like "Ships That Could Think" have appeal. Mention the parts of the article you think create a mood of mystery.

2. **Earthquakes** *pages 252–259*

   This science article explains the causes and effects of earthquakes.

   Observe a happening in nature such as hailstorm, thunderstorm, snowstorm, and so on . The happening can be one that is ordinary rather than exciting. Write an eyewitness report of what happened. Use facts from your experience to help you describe the happening.

3. **Sparky** *pages 260–263*

   "Sparky" is an essay about someone who had little reason to believe he would one day be a major success. The writer describes how Charles Schulz succeeded in spite of being labeled a loser in his early years.

   Write a paragraph describing what you think was the key to Charles Schulz's success.

4. **The Roswell Incident** *pages 264–267*

   After reading this informational article, what do you believe about the possibility that aliens landed here decades ago?

   Write a brief opinion statement about the article. Did reading "The Roswell Incident" cause you to look at information about aliens in a different way? Did the article answer your questions, or did it raise even more? Do you think the writer did a good job of covering a difficult subject?

UNIT 8 WRITING ASSIGNMENT: EYEWITNESS REPORT

As the selections of this unit show, nonfiction can explain, spark questions, and even inspire. Spend a brief period of time observing a happening. Then use what you observed to write an eyewitness report. The template on the following page will help you record and organize your observations.

Observation Chart for Eyewitness Report

Event or subject observed:	
Visual Details:	
Sounds:	
Smells:	
Tastes:	
Feel/Textures:	
Other Features: duration, function, condition, location, importance, value	

Revising Skill: Sequence

When writing an eyewitness report, organize the events in the order in which they happened. This makes the report easy to follow. Which sentence shows the events in order?

A. Lightning struck the ship. A ship went out to sea. The ship broke in half.

B. A ship went out to sea. Lightning struck the ship. The ship broke in half.

Write the following events from the article, "The Roswell Incident" in the order in which they happened.

Max examined a piece of shiny metal.

Mac telephoned the air force base at nearby Roswell.

Mac saw the ground littered with shiny metal pieces.

Staff from the Roswell base arrived at Mac's ranch.

1. _____

_____

2. _____

_____

3. _____

_____

4. _____

_____

Quick-Fix Editing Machine p. 198

Editing Tip: Correcting Fragments

If a sentence does not express a complete thought, it may be missing a subject or a predicate.

Incorrect: Spent a great deal of time on his drawings.

Correct: He spent a great deal of time on his drawings.

Revise Your Eyewitness Report

When you revise your eyewitness report, make sure that the events are in the order in which they happened. All of your sentences need a subject and a predicate.

Writing Prompts

Unit 9 Making Adjustments

1. The Jade Stone *pages 270–280*

The writer probably wrote "The Jade Stone" to raise questions such as Should artists be free to create whatever art they choose? Should an artist think of his or her audience when creating a work or simply follow his or her inspiration? Should people in authority have the final word about how a work of art should be created?

Take a side. In a brief, persuasive paragraph, state your answer to or position on one of the questions. Try to convince readers that your position is a sound one. Refer to the happenings in "The Jade Stone" in your essay.

2. The Stolen Party *pages 282–293*

"The Stolen Party" is an unusual title. There's a party but no actual theft takes place. Think about the characters in the story and how the story ends.

Write a brief interpretation of the title of the story. Use details from "The Stolen Party" to explain your interpretation. Whom do you think would describe Luciana's birthday party as a "stolen" one? What reasons might that character have for feeling this way?

3. Acceptance *pages 294–303*

In reading "Acceptance," you learned about issues that matter to a dedicated animal scientist.

Imagine that Jane Goodall plans to visit your school. What do you think she would say to persuade young people to become animal scientists themselves? Write a paragraph from a persuasive speech that Jane Goodall might make to your school.

4. Growing Up in a World of Darkness *pages 304–317*

This biography gives you a close-up view of the childhood of Stevie Wonder. You discover how his early fascination with music becomes a lifelong career.

What do you think is the right time for a talented entertainer to go into show business? Is ten years old too soon? Write a persuasive paragraph that expresses your views. Think about the qualities Stevie Wonder had. Think about the ways his family supported him. Support your views with details from the biography.

> **UNIT 9 WRITING ASSIGNMENT: PERSUASIVE ESSAY**
>
> The characters and real people of this unit make different kinds of adjustments. Imagine the editor of a teen e-magazine has asked you to encourage young people to be more physically active. Write a persuasive essay about the small adjustments many young people can make to become more fit. You can use the template on the next page to help you compose your persuasive essay.

Persuasive Essay

Introduction

What are the issues?

What is your opinion?

Body

Supporting Evidence:	Supporting Evidence:	Supporting Evidence:

Conclusion

Summarize your opinion.

Revising Skill: Using Appropriate Language

When writing, use the language your audience expects and understands. For parents, teachers, and other adults, choose words that are more formal. When writing to friends, you may relax and use slang. Which sentence might a teenager write to a friend?

A. Yo! What's up dude?

B. Hello, Ms. Daniels. How are you?

Rewrite each sentence for the audience in parentheses.

1. Hey man, what's the rush? (emperor or political leader)

_____

_____

2. What are you wearing to the concert? (friend)

_____

_____

3. I breezed through that book. (teacher)

_____

_____

4. Your shortie could use a hug. (mother)

_____

_____

Quick-Fix Editing Machine p. 199

Editing Tip: Correcting Run-Ons

When you are writing, be sure that you don't write two sentences as though they are one.

Incorrect: I like parties, I'm going to Luciana's party tomorrow.

Correct: I like parties. I'm going to Luciana's party tomorrow.

Revise Your Persuasive Essay

When you revise your essay, be sure that the language you use is right for your audience. Separate any run-on sentences.

Writing Prompts

Unit 10 Appearances Can Fool You

1. Some People *pages 320–321*

The people in the first half of this poem are different from the people in the second half. How are they different? Are there ways in which they are alike?

Write a paragraph that compares and contrasts the people in the first and second verses.

2. Almost Human *pages 322–325*

This poem is written from the point of view of a dolphin. The dolphin watches people and points out the things people do. The dolphin seems amused. Pick your favorite animal. Think about how this animal might view people. Do people amuse the animal?

Write a paragraph about what your favorite animal might say about people.

3. Nikki-Rosa *pages 328–331*

This poem is written in free verse. It has no regular pattern of rhyme, rhythm, or line length. Sometimes free verse sounds like conversation. "Nikki-Rosa" tells about life growing up in Chicago. Where did you grow up? What was it like? What did you do? Where did you go?

Write a poem in free verse about your school. Include the sights, smells, sounds, and people that make going to school a memorable experience. Remember, your poem does not have to rhyme.

UNIT 10 WRITING ASSIGNMENT: OPINION STATEMENT

Reread all four poems in this unit. Select the one you like the best. Write an opinion statement telling why you like it the best. Give three reasons why you like the poem. Support your reasons with examples from the poem. Your reasons could include the message, the form, the figurative language, the subject matter, the rhythm, the imagery, or something else that appeals to you. Use the template on the next page to help you organize your ideas.

Writing Template

Name_____

Opinion Statement

Tell which poem you like best.

Reason 1: Example from poem

Reason 2: Example from poem

Reason 3: Example from poem

Conclusion:

Revising Skill: Quoting

Showing examples helps to illustrate your opinion. **Quotation marks** show that you are picking up the author's exact words. Which sentence shows how to use the author's exact words?

> **A.** The line "Sunday dinner isn't sunny" is an example of how the poet repeats sounds.
>
> **B.** The line Sunday dinner isn't sunny is an example of how the poet repeats sounds.

Use each of the following lines of poetry in a sentence. Use quotation marks to show you are using the author's exact words.

Come and see the people dear.

All shiny in your mind

From the turkey's point of view

1. _____

_____

2. _____

_____

3. _____

_____

Editing Tip: Consistent Point of View

Be sure to keep the same point of view throughout your writing. Since it is your opinion, remember to use I or me.

Incorrect: This poem rhymes. You think rhyme is cool.

Correct: This poem rhymes. I think rhyme is cool.

Revising Your Opinion Statement

When you pick up an author's exact words, remember to put them in quotation marks. Don't forget to keep the same point of view.

Writing Prompts

Unit 11 Bridges to History

1. The Invaders *pages 334–339*

Think about the ending of "The Invaders." Up to that point, you probably thought you were reading a different kind of tale. Or you may have spotted certain clues that led you to expect the unexpected.

Write a response to "The Invaders." Share your reactions to the story. Reveal why you were or were not surprised by the ending. Why do you think the writer wrote the story in this way?

2. Weapons of War *pages 340–347*

This article presents the many ways in which American colonists fought for freedom from Great Britain.

Write a comparison-and-contrast paragraph that describes how American soldiers were different from British soldiers. Think of each group's goals, appearance, and training. Use details from the article.

3. The New Mother *pages 348–363*

Something important was missing in the life of young Abe Lincoln. When Sarah Lincoln becomes a part of his life, changes begin happening almost immediately.

Think about the arrival of Sarah Lincoln and its effect on Abe. Write a cause-effect description of Abe's experience in "The New Mother."

4. The Ballad of John Henry *pages 364–369*

"The Ballad of John Henry" is a great American song sung by railroad workers. These workers often sang songs because hearing rhythmic sounds made working easier.

Are songs and stories about past heroes still worthwhile today? Do they still have the power to entertain or to inspire? Write an opinion statement. Include your reactions to "The Ballad of John Henry" in your statement.

5. *from* California Gold Days *pages 370–379*

The Forty-Niners described in this article brought to the West their hopes for a brighter future.

What was life like for them once they reached their destinations? After doing brief research, write a paragraph of a research report about one Forty-Niner family. Include details you found.

6. Rabbit Foot: A Story of the Peacemaker *pages 380–385*

In this oral history, a few Native American groups are locked in a conflict. They come together to listen to a tale that seems quite simple but contains a very strong message about peace.

Find out about a peace effort—past or present. Perhaps it was a single event or a series of events. Write a report that explores how a group that calls for peace attempts to reach others.

UNIT 11 WRITING ASSIGNMENT: RESEARCH REPORT

The selections in this unit span over a century of happening in America. They extend from arrival of the first pioneers to the growth of the railroads. What period of early American history interests you? Write a research paper on one person or event from America's first one hundred years. Use the template on the following page to gather evidence and support for your ideas.

Research Report

Thesis statement:

Evidence:

Support:

Evidence:

Support:

Evidence:

Support:

Conclusion:

Revising Skill: Varying Sentences

Reading one long sentence after another can be boring. Reading too many short sentences in a row can be confusing. Writers vary their sentences to make writing interesting and easy to understand. They use conjunctions, sequence words, and transitions to help. Which paragraph reads more smoothly.

A. The Forty-Niners took risks because they wanted a new way of life. Although they were going into strange lands, they were willing to face the dangers. They had hope. They had plans for the future.

B. The Forty-Niners took risks. They wanted a new way of life. They were going into strange lands. They were willing to face the dangers. They had hope. They had plans for the future.

Rewrite the following paragraph to make the sentences read smoothly. Use words such as *but, and,* and *because* to combine related sentences and to show transitions.

Imagine riding in a wagon. Imagine bouncing over bumpy, unpaved roads. The Forty-Niners were happy to reach new homes. They had overcome many troubles. Many of their dangers had come to an end. A new set of hardships had just begun.

_____

_____

_____

_____

_____

_____

_____

_____

Editing Tip: Fact Checking

Research reports usually include many facts. Readers expect the facts to be accurate. If possible, use more than one source to check facts. If there's space, flesh out the facts with details.

Incorrect: In 1848, a great movement to the west began.

Correct: In 1848, someone discovered gold in California. By 1849, many people from the east began to move in great numbers to the west.

Revise Your Research Report

Skim your research report. To make your sentences easy to understand, use conjunctions to vary your sentences. Check to see that your facts are accurate and don't cause readers confusion.

Unit 12 Reader's Choice

1. *from* **Hiroshima** *pages 388–404*

In this novel, two sisters experience the realities of war. In the city of Hiroshima on August 6, 1945, many ordinary people—like Sachi's sister and classmates—lost their lives.

Think about what happened in Hiroshima on that terrible day. Think about victims of war that you may know. Write a tribute to people who become the victims of war. Include your reactions to the incidents you read about in the story.

2. *from* **Anne Frank: Child of the Holocaust** *pages 406–425*

Anne Frank was a young person whose behavior or attitudes were much like young people of today. This biography reveals that she first described going into hiding with her family as a "vacation" and an "adventure."

Think about the ways you've seen people deal with danger or tragedy. What personal qualities do you think help people to face such terrible situations? In your opinion, are young people naturally more positive? Are young people better equipped than older people to overcome tough times? Explore these questions by writing an opinion statement. Use incidents or details from Anne Frank: Child of the Holocaust to support your views.

3. **Black Whiteness: Admiral Byrd Alone in Antarctica** *pages 426–449*

This story tells what an explorer sacrifices to help advance scientific knowledge.

Think of a modern-day explorer or adventurer. Write a brief comparison-and-contrast of that person and Admiral Byrd. What tools or abilities does that person have that probably weren't available during Admiral Byrd's time? What explorers of today find it necessary to work alone?

UNIT 12 WRITING ASSIGNMENT: AUTOBIOGRAPHICAL INCIDENT

Think about the major happenings that have occurred so far in your lifetime. Think of what you've witnessed directly or have heard a lot about. Pick one event or happening that came closest to touching your daily life. Write about that experience as an autobiographical incident. Tell what the incident meant to you. Use the template on the following page. In the first box briefly identify the incident. Then answer the questions in each box.

Autobiographical Incident

Memory:

Who was there?

What happened?

What sights, sounds, smells, tastes, and textures can I remember?

What did I feel?

What did it mean to me?

Name_____

Revising Skill: Sensory Details

Sensory details appeal to the senses. They can vividly paint pictures in readers' minds and give readers the impression of experiencing what they're reading. Which sentence is more interesting?

A. Admiral Byrd stood in the strong wind.

B. Admiral Bryd stood in the biting wind that attacked his bare face.

Complete the following sentences using the correct sensory details.

1. The _____ match flame touched the _____ wick of

   the metal lantern. An _____ smell filled his nostrils.

   (Use these details: frozen, flickering, oily)

2. Snow under his _____ boots _____ noisily as

   Admiral Byrd tried to move his _____ legs forward.

   (Use these details: quivery, heavy, crunched)

3. A _____ feeling began to warm Admiral Byrd as heat from the

   _____ fire crept through the _____ layers of his

   clothing.

   (Use these details: thick, blazing, tingling)

Editing Tip: Misplaced Phrases

A sentence can be confusing or even funny when a phrase is in the wrong place. Be sure you write a phrase that is close to the word or words it modifies.

Incorrect: Writing in his diary, the candlelight revealed Admiral Bryd.

Correct: The candlelight revealed Admiral Byrd writing in his diary.

Revise Your Autobiographical Incident

Go back to the autobiographical incident you wrote. How well did you introduce and re-create the incident? Check to see if you included sensory details to bring scenes to life for readers. Check your sentences to be sure that all phrases are in the right place.

You've worked hard on your assignment. Don't let misplaced commas, sentence fragments, and missing details lower your grade. Use this Quick-Fix Editing Guide to help you detect grammatical errors and make your writing more precise.

Fixing Errors

What's the problem? Part of a sentence has been left out.

Why does it matter? A fragment doesn't convey a complete thought.

What should you do about it? Find out what is missing and add it.

What's the Problem?

What's the Problem?	Quick Fix
A. A subject is missing. Practiced for a whole week.	**Add a subject.** **My friends and I** practiced for a whole week.
B. A predicate is missing. Auditions in the school auditorium.	**Add a predicate.** Auditions **were held** in the school auditorium.
C. Both a subject and a predicate are missing. For almost a month.	**Add a subject and a predicate to make an independent clause.** **We rehearsed** for almost a month.
D. A dependent clause is treated as if it were a sentence. Because we all wore costumes.	**Combine the fragment with an independent clause.** **The performance was exciting** because we all wore costumes. **OR** **Delete the conjunction.** ~~Because~~ We all wore costumes.

Run-On Sentences

What's the problem? Two or more sentences have been written as though they were a single sentence.

Why does it matter? A run-on sentence doesn't show where one idea ends and another begins.

What should you do about it? Find the best way to separate ideas or to show the proper relationship between them.

What's the Problem?

Quick Fix

A. The end mark separating two sentences is missing.

Dolapo raced up the court her defender closed in.

Add an end mark to divide the run-on into two sentences.

Dolapo raced up the court. **H**er defender closed in.

B. Two sentences are separated only by a comma.

Dolapo faked a shot, her defender wasn't fooled.

Add a coordinating conjunction.

Dolapo faked a shot, **but** her defender wasn't fooled.

OR

Change the comma to a semicolon.

Dolapo faked a shot; her defender wasn't fooled.

OR

Replace the comma with an end mark and start a new sentence.

Dolapo faked a shot. **H**er defender wasn't fooled.

OR

Change one of the independent clauses to a dependent clause by adding a subordinating conjunction.

Although Dolapo faked a shot, her

What's the problem? A verb does not agree with its subject in number.

Why does it matter? Readers may think your work is careless.

What should you do about it? Identify the subject and use a verb that matches it in number.

What's the Problem?

Quick Fix

A. The first helping verb in a verb phrase does not agree with the subject.

We **has** been enjoying tea during our stay in London.

Decide whether the subject is singular or plural, and make the helping verb agree with it.

We **have** been enjoying tea during our stay in London.

B. The contraction doesn't agree with its subject.

Many **Britons doesn't** work at 4:00 P.M. because of teatime.

Use a contraction that agrees with the subject.

Many **Britons don't** work at 4:00 P.M. because of teatime.

C. A singular verb is used with a compound subject that contains *and.*

Many **natives and** an **occasional tourist visits** this fancy tearoom.

Use a plural verb.

Many **natives and** an occasional **tourist visit** this fancy tearoom.

D. A verb doesn't agree with the nearer part of a compound subject containing *or* or *nor.*

Neither the waiters nor the **owner want** any unhappy customers.

Make the verb agree with the nearer part.

Neither the waiters nor the **owner wants** any unhappy customers.

E. A verb doesn't agree with an indefinite-pronoun subject.

Each of the servers **give** customers undivided attention.

Decide whether the pronoun is singular or plural, and make the verb agree with it.

Each of the servers **gives** patrons undivided attention.

What's the Problem?	Quick Fix
F. A collective noun referring to individuals is treated as singular. The **staff dresses** in formal attire.	Use a plural verb if the collective noun refers to individuals. The **staff dress** in formal attire.
G. A singular subject ending in *s* or *ics* is mistaken for a plural. **Politics are** often discussed in the tearoom.	Watch out for these nouns and use singular verbs with them. **Politics is** often discussed in the tearoom.
H. A verb doesn't agree with the true subject of a sentence beginning with *here* or *there*. **There is** tea, finger sandwiches, and cakes on the menu.	Mentally turn the sentence around so that the subject comes first, and make the verb agree with it. There **are tea, finger sandwiches, and cakes** on the menu.
I. A verb agrees with the object of a preposition rather than with its subject. A tea in some **areas tend** to be a meal.	Mentally block out the prepositional phrase, and make the verb agree with the subject. A **tea** ~~in some areas~~ **tends** to be a meal.
J. A plural verb is used with a period of time or an amount. **Two hours are** all the time we had to enjoy our tea.	Use a singular verb. **Two hours is** all the time we had to enjoy our tea.

What's the problem? A pronoun does not agree in number, person, or gender with its antecedent, or an antecedent is unclear.

Why does it matter? Lack of agreement or unclear antecedents can confuse your readers.

What should you do about it? Find the antecedent and make the pronoun agree with it, or rewrite the sentence to make the antecedent clear.

What's the Problem?	Quick Fix
A. A pronoun doesn't agree in number with its antecedent. A computer user **group** has **their** advantages.	**Make the pronoun agree in number with the antecedent.** A computer user **group** has **its** advantages.
B. A pronoun doesn't agree in person or in gender with its antecedent. **Ernesto** has discovered **you** can learn valuable tips from others.	**Make the pronoun agree with its antecedent.** **Ernesto** has discovered **he** can learn valuable tips from others.
C. A pronoun doesn't agree with an indefinite-pronoun antecedent. **Anyone** who owns a computer can increase **their** knowledge by sharing with a group.	**Decide whether the indefinite pronoun is singular or plural, and make the pronoun agree with it.** **Anyone** who owns a computer can increase **his or her** knowledge by sharing with a group.
D. A pronoun could refer to more than one noun. **Irma** and **Kira** attended a meeting. **She** learned a lot.	**Substitute a noun for the pronoun to make the reference clear.** **Irma** and **Kira** attended a meeting. **Kira** learned a lot.
E. A pronoun agrees with a word or a phrase that comes between it and its antecedent. **Kira,** like many **people,** may not know a lot about their computer.	**Mentally block out the word or phrase and change the pronoun so that it agrees with its antecedent.** **Kira,** ~~like many people,~~ may not know a lot about **her** computer.

Incorrect Pronoun Case

What's the problem? A pronoun is in the wrong case.

Why does it matter? Readers may think your work is careless, especially if you are writing a school paper or formal letter.

What should you do about it? Identify how the pronoun is being used, and replace it with the correct form.

What's the Problem?	Quick Fix
A. A pronoun that follows a linking verb is in the wrong case. The most experienced computer user **is her.**	**Always use the subject case after a linking verb.** The most experienced computer user **is she.**
B. A pronoun used as an object is in the wrong case. Kira **showed** Kent and **I** some shortcuts.	**Always use an object pronoun as a direct object, an indirect object, or the object of a preposition.** Kira **showed** Kent and **me** some shortcuts.
C. A contraction is used instead of a possessive pronoun. **You're** computer skills have really improved.	**Use a possessive pronoun.** **Your** computer skills have really improved.
D. A pronoun in a compound subject is in the wrong case. A few members and **me** talked about software problems.	**Always use the subject case when a pronoun is used as part of a compound subject.** A few members and **I** talked about software problems.
E. A pronoun followed by an identifying noun is in the wrong case. A software company asked **we members** to test a new game	**Mentally block out the identifying noun to test for the correct case.** A software company asked **us** ~~members~~ to test a new game.

6 Who and Whom

What's the problem? The pronoun *who* or *whom* is used incorrectly.

Why does it matter? When writers use *who* and *whom* correctly, readers are more likely to take their ideas seriously.

What should you do about it? Decide how the pronoun functions in the sentence, and then choose the correct form.

What's the Problem?	Quick Fix
A. *Whom* is incorrectly used as a subject pronoun. **Whom knows** the origin of origami?	Use *who* as a subject pronoun. **Who knows** the origin of origami?
B. *Whom* is incorrectly used as a predicate pronoun. The expert on origami **is whom?**	Use *who* as a predicate pronoun. The expert on origami **is who?**
C. *Who* is incorrectly used as a direct object. **Who can** we **ask** about these paper sculptures?	Use *whom* as a direct object. **Whom can** we **ask** about these paper sculptures?
D. *Who* is incorrectly used as the object of a preposition. These instructions are **for who?**	Use *whom* as the object of a preposition. These instructions are **for whom?**
E. *Who* is incorrectly used as an indirect object. You **asked who** these questions?	Use *whom* as an indirect object. You **asked whom** these questions?
F. *Who's* is incorrectly used as the possessive pronoun *whose*. **Who's sculpture** is most likely to win first prize?	Use *whose* to show possession. **Whose sculpture** is most likely to win first prize?

Confusing Comparisons

What's the problem? The wrong form of an adjective or adverb is used in making a comparison.

Why does it matter? Comparisons that are not worded correctly can be confusing.

What should you do about it? Use a form that makes the comparison clear.

What's the Problem?

A. Both _-er_ and _more_ or _-est_ and _most_ are used in making a comparison.

Long ago, chariot races in Rome were **more dangerouser** than any modern auto race.

The best driver was not the one who raced **most fastest.**

B. A comparative form is used where a superlative form is needed.

The best driver was the one who was **more** successful at forcing other drivers to crash.

C. A superlative form is used where a comparative form is needed.

However, crowds cheered **most** loudly for land battles than for chariot races.

Quick Fix

Delete one of the forms from the sentence.

Long ago, chariot races in Rome were **more dangerouser** than any modern auto race.

The best driver was not the one who raced **most fastest.**

Use the superlative form when comparing more than two things.

The best driver was the one who was **most** successful at forcing other drivers to crash.

Use the comparative form when comparing two things.

However, crowds cheered **more** loudly for land battles than for chariot races.

What's the problem? The wrong form or tense of a verb is used.

Why does it matter? Readers may regard your work as careless or find it confusing.

What should you do about it? Change the verb to the correct form or tense.

What's the Problem?

What's the Problem?	Quick Fix
A. The wrong form of a verb is used with a helping verb. Many towns **have grew** with the expansion of railroads.	Always use a participle form with a helping verb. Many towns **have grown** with the expansion of railroads.
B. A helping verb is missing. In the late 1800s, herds of cattle **raised** in Texas.	**Add a helping verb.** In the late 1800s, herds of cattle **were raised** in Texas.
C. A past participle is used incorrectly. Cowhands **gone** to the end of the rail lines with their cattle.	**To write about the past, use the past form of a verb.** Cowhands **went** to the end of the rail lines with their cattle. **OR** **Change the verb to the past perfect form by adding a helping verb.** Cowhands **had gone** to the end of the rail lines with their cattle.
D. Different tenses are used in the same sentence even though no change in time has occurred. Cow towns **sprang** up around the rail lines, and more **appear** farther west as the railroads **did.**	**Use the same tense throughout the sentence.** Cow towns **sprang** up around the rail lines, and more **appeared** farther west as the railroads **did.**

Missing or Misplaced Commas

What's the problem? Commas are missing or are used incorrectly.

Why does it matter? Incorrect use of commas can make sentences hard to follow.

What should you do about it? Figure out where commas are needed, and add them as necessary.

What's the Problem?

A. A comma is missing from a compound sentence.

The cover of this book is torn and the pages are missing.

B. A comma is incorrectly placed after a closing quotation mark.

"I'll have to take this book back to the library", said Tristan.

C. A comma is missing before the conjunction in a series.

Ivan, LaToya and Keiko will meet him there after school.

D. A comma is missing after an introductory word, phrase, or clause.

Fortunately Tristan proved that he did not damage the book.

E. Commas are missing around an appositive or a clause that is not essential to the meaning of the sentence.

The librarian Tristan's aunt assured us that the book will be repaired immediately.

Quick Fix

Add a comma before the coordinating conjunction.

The cover of this book is torn, and the pages are missing.

Always put a comma before a closing quotation mark.

"I'll have to take this book back to the library," said Tristan.

Add a comma.

Ivan, LaToya, and Keiko will meet him there after school.

Add a comma after an introductory word, phrase, or clause.

Fortunately, Tristan proved that he did not damage the book.

Add commas to set off the appositive or clause.

The librarian, Tristan's aunt, assured us that the book will be repaired immediately.

BOOKS FOR INDEPENDENT READING LEVEL III

BOOK	ANNOTATION
Joyful Noise: Poems for Two Voices Fleischman, Paul; 1988 44 pp. Mean DRP: N/A	Poems about insects
American Sports Poems Knudson, R. R., 0 Swenson, May; 1988 226 pp. Mean DRP: N/A	An anthology of sports poems
My Own True Name Mora, Pat; 2000 81 pp. Mean DRP: N/A	A collection of poems about growing up Mexican-American in the Southwest
Falling Up Silverstein, Shel; 1996 176 pp. Mean DRP: N/A	An anthology of humorous poems
A Fire in My Hands Soto, Gary; 1990 63 pp. Mean DRP: N/A	Gary Soto's personal poems about growing up in California in the '60s
Neighborhood Odes Soto, Gary; 1992 70 pp. Mean DRP: N/A	Poems in praise of growing up in a Latino neighborhood
It Came from Ohio!: My Life as a Writer Stine, R. L.; 1997 140 pp. Mean DRP: 50	Nonfiction: R. L. Stine, author of the Goosebumps and Fear Street series, tells about his childhood in Ohio.
A Wrinkle in Time L'Engle, Madeleine; 1962 211 pp. Mean DRP: 51	Meg and her little brother, Charles, travel through time in search of their father, a prisoner on an alien planet.
My Life with Chimpanzees Goodall, Jane; 1988 123 pp. Mean DRP: 52	Nonfiction: Jane Goodall studies wild chimpanzees in Africa.
Number the Stars Lowry, Lois; 1989 137 pp. Mean DRP: 52	Annemarie, a Dutch girl, and Ellen, a Jewish girl, are best friends. Annemarie tries to save Ellen from the Nazis.

BOOK	ANNOTATION
The Story of Harriet Tubman, Conductor of the Underground Railroad McMullan, Kate; 1991 108 pp. Mean DRP: 52	Nonfiction: The story of Harriet Tubman, an escaped slave who led over 300 slaves to freedom
Marco Polo: His Notebook Roth, Susan L.; 1990 30 pp. Mean DRP: 52	Nonfiction: The journal of 17-year-old Marco Polo as he begins an incredible adventure in 1271
Taking Sides Soto, Gary; 1991 138 pp. Mean DRP: 52	Fourteen-year-old Lincoln Mendoza's loyalties are divided when his new suburban basketball team plays against his old team from the barrio.
Marching to Freedom: The Story of Martin Luther King Jr. Milton, Joyce; 1987 92 pp. Mean DRP: 53	Nonfiction: A biography of Martin Luther King, Jr.
Island of the Blue Dolphins O'Dell, Scott; 1960 189 pp. Mean DRP: 53	Karana, an Indian girl, lives alone on an island for 18 years.
Woodsong Paulsen, Gary; 1990 132 pp. Mean DRP: 53	Nonfiction: Author Gary Paulsen tells about his life and adventures with his sled dogs.
The Bronze Bow Speare, Elizabeth George; 1961 254 pp. Mean DRP: 53	Daniel's parents are killed, and all he can think about is revenge. Something happens to change his mind.
Roll of Thunder, Hear My Cry Taylor, Mildred D.; 1976 276 pp. Mean DRP: 53	Cassie Logan, a young black girl, struggles to remain proud and independent during the Depression in Mississippi.
Dicey's Song Voigt, Cynthia; 1982 196 pp. Mean DRP: 53	Dicey Tillerman brings her brothers and sister to live with their eccentric grandmother.
The Education of Little Tree Carter, Forrest; 1976 216 pp. Mean DRP: 54	Forrest Carter remembers living with his Cherokee grandparents during the 1930s.

BOOK	ANNOTATION
Memories of Anne Frank: Reflections of a Childhood Friend Gold, Alison Leslie; 1997 135 pp. Mean DRP:54	Nonfiction: Hannah Goslar, Anne Frank's close friend and classmate in Amsterdam, shares her memories of Anne before the war separated them.
The Lion, the Witch, and the Wardrobe Lewis, C. S.; 1950 186 pp. Mean DRP: 54	Peter, Edmund, Suzy, and Lucy magically pass through a wardrobe into the land of Narnia.
The Story of Nin: The Chimp Who Learned Language Michel, Anna; 1980 59 pp. Mean DRP: 54	Nonfiction: The story of Nin, a chimpanzee who was raised like a human baby
Your Two Brains Stafford, Patricia; 1986 75 pp. Mean DRP: 54	Nonfiction: Informational book about the function of the left and right sides of the brain
Stuart Little White, E. B.; 1945 131 pp. Mean DRP: 54	A humorous story about Stuart, second son of the Littles, who is only 2 inches tall and a mouse!
I'm Nobody! Who Are You? Barth, Edna; 1971 128 pp. Mean DRP: 55	Nonfiction: The life and times of the famous poet Emily Dickinson
My Life as an Astronaut Bean, Alan; 1988 105 pp. Mean DRP: 55	Nonfiction: Alan Bean tells how he came to be an astronaut and what it felt like being part of the Apollo crew.
Johnny Tremain Forbes, Esther; 1943 256 pp. Mean DRP: 55	In 1773, Johny Tremain, a young apprentice silversmith, becomes involved in the American Revolution.
Lost Star: The Story of Amelia Earhart Lauber, Patricia; 1988 106 pp. Mean DRP: 55	Nonfiction: The story of Amelia Earhart, the first woman to fly solo across the Atlantic Ocean
Baseball in April and Other Stories Soto, Gary; 1990 137 pp. Mean DRP: 55	Eleven short stories about life in California's Central Valley
Call It Courage Sperry, Armstrong; 1963 92 pp. Mean DRP: 55	Ten-year-old Mafatu fears the sea but sets out to sea in a canoe to prove he is not a coward.

BOOK	ANNOTATION
Pride of Puerto Rico: The Life of Roberto Clemente Walker, Paul Robert; 1988 157 pp. Mean DRP: 55	Nonfiction: A biography of baseball legend Roberto Clemente
Anne Frank: Child of the Holocaust Brown, Gene; 1991 64 pp. Mean DRP: 56	Nonfiction: The story of Anne Frank, a 13-year-old girl who kept a diary while she was hiding from the Nazis
The Midwife's Apprentice Cushman, Karen; 1995 122 pp. Mean DRP: 56	A homeless girl in 14th-century England is taken in by a midwife named Jane, who makes her her apprentice.
Boy: Tales of Childhood Dahl, Roald; 1984 176 pp. Mean DRP: 56	Nonfiction: Roald Dahl recalls his boyhood in England, summers in Norway, and the "Great Mouse Plot" of 1924.
Nelson Mandela Falstein, Mark; 1994 73 pp. Mean DRP 56	Nonfiction: The story of Nelson Mandela's fight against apartheid
Frozen Man Getz, David; 1994 68 pp. Mean DRP: 56	Nonfiction: Scientists use clues to re- create the death and life of a man who died more than 5,000 years ago.
Great Lives: Human Rights Jacobs, William Jay; 1990 278 pp. Mean DRP: 56	Nonfiction: A portrayal of 29 people who contributed to the struggle for human rights in the United States
The Giver Lowry, Lois; 1993 180 pp. Mean DRP: 56	Jonas discovers the truth about his "perfect" society when he is chosen to become a "receiver of memories."
How Do We Dream? and Other Questions About Your Body Myers, Jack; 1992 60 pp. Mean DRP: 56	Nonfiction: Scientists answer questions about the human body.
Satchel Paige: All-Time Baseball Great Rubin, Robert; 1974 157 pp. Mean DRP: 56	Nonfiction: The life and career of one of baseball's greatest pitchers, Leroy "Satchel" Paige

BOOK	ANNOTATION
Knots in My Yo-Yo String: The Autobiography of a Kid Spinelli, Jerry; 1998 148 pp. Mean DRP: 56	Nonfiction: The creator of Maniac Magee recalls his childhood.
Journey to Topaz Uchida, Yoshiko; 1971 149 pp. Mean DRP: 56	Nonfiction: When Pearl Harbor is bombed, Yuki's life suddenly changes.
Earthquake!: San Francisco, 1906 Wilson, Kate; 1993 62 pp. Mean DRP: 56	People unite to survive when a terrible earthquake devastates San Francisco in 1906.
Arctic Explorer: The Story of Matthew Henson Ferris, Jeri; 1989 80 pp. Mean DRP: 57	Nonfiction: The story of Matthew Henson, a black explorer who reached the North Pole alongside Robert Peary in April 1909
Seeing Earth from Space Lauber, Patricia; 1990 80 pp. Mean DRP: 57	Nonfiction: A look at photographs taken from space
Michael Jordan Lovitt, Chip; 1995 186 pp. Mean DRP: 57	Nonfiction: The life and career of one of basketball's greatest legends

Reading Log

Name _____ **Date** _____

Title/Author	Genre	Date Finished	Reactions

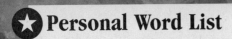
Use these pages to build your personal vocabulary. As
you read the selections, take time to mark unfamiliar
words. These should be words that seem interesting or
important enough to add to your permanent vocabulary.
After reading, look up the meanings of these words and
record the information below. For each word, write a
sentence that shows its correct use.

Review your list from time to time. Try to put these words
into use in your writing and conversation.

Word: _____

Selection: _____

Page/Line: _____ / _____

Part of Speech: _____

Definition: _____

_____

_____

Sentence: _____

_____

_____

_____

Word: _____

Selection: _____

Page/Line: _____ / _____

Part of Speech: _____

Definition: _____

_____

_____

Sentence: _____

_____

_____

_____

Word: _____

Selection: _____

Page/Line: _____ / _____

Part of Speech: _____

Definition: _____

_____

_____

Sentence: _____

_____

_____

Word: _____

Selection: _____

Page/Line: _____ / _____

Part of Speech: _____

Definition: _____

_____

_____

Sentence: _____

_____

_____

Name_____

Word: _____

Selection: _____

Page/Line: _____ / _____

Part of Speech: _____

Definition: _____

_____

_____

Sentence: _____

_____

_____

_____

Word: _____

Selection: _____

Page/Line: _____ / _____

Part of Speech: _____

Definition: _____

_____

_____

Sentence: _____

_____

_____

_____

Word: _____

Selection: _____

Page/Line: _____ / _____

Part of Speech: _____

Definition: _____

_____

_____

Sentence: _____

_____

_____

Word: _____

Selection: _____

Page/Line: _____ / _____

Part of Speech: _____

Definition: _____

_____

_____

Sentence: _____

_____

_____

Word: _____

Selection: _____

Page/Line: _____ / _____

Part of Speech: _____

Definition: _____

_____

_____

Sentence: _____

_____

_____

Word: _____

Selection: _____

Page/Line: _____ / _____

Part of Speech: _____

Definition: _____

_____

_____

Sentence: _____

_____

_____

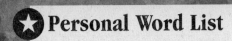
Word: _____

Selection: _____

Page/Line: _____ / _____

Part of Speech: _____

Definition: _____

_____

_____

Sentence: _____

_____

_____

_____

_____

Word: _____

Selection: _____

Page/Line: _____ / _____

Part of Speech: _____

Definition: _____

_____

_____

Sentence: _____

_____

_____

_____

_____

Word: _____

Selection: _____

Page/Line: _____ / _____

Part of Speech: _____

Definition: _____

_____

_____

Sentence: _____

_____

_____

Word: _____

Selection: _____

Page/Line: _____ / _____

Part of Speech: _____

Definition: _____

_____

_____

Sentence: _____

_____

_____

_____

_____

Word: _____

Selection: _____

Page/Line: _____ / _____

Part of Speech: _____

Definition: _____

_____

_____

Sentence: _____

_____

_____

Word: _____

Selection: _____

Page/Line: _____ / _____

Part of Speech: _____

Definition: _____

_____

_____

Sentence: _____

_____

_____